LECTURES IN ADVANCED MATHEMATICS

WILLIAM J. LEVEQUE · EDITOR

HAROLD DAVENPORT: *1. Multiplicative Number Theory*

THOMAS STORER: *2. Cyclotomy and Difference Sets*

ERWIN ENGELER: *3. Formal Languages: Automata and Structures*

ADRIANO M. GARSIA: *4. Topics in Almost Everywhere Convergence*

ADRIANO M. GARSIA

University of California

TOPICS in ALMOST EVERYWHERE CONVERGENCE

MARKHAM PUBLISHING COMPANY · CHICAGO

Printed in the United States of America
Library of Congress Catalog Number: 70-91020
Standard Book Number: **8410-1910-X**

PREFACE

These notes cover the contents of lectures delivered in the probability seminar at the California Institute of Technology in the academic year 1964–1965 and in the analysis seminar at La Jolla in the fall of 1966 and the fall of 1968.

The material is divided into four chapters. In the first chapter we cover some basic principles related to almost everywhere convergence. These are theorems which state that under rather general circumstances establishing an a.e. convergence result is equivalent to deducing a certain maximal inequality.

In the second chapter, after establishing some basic facts about positive operators, including the maximal ergodic inequalities, we present proofs of the ergodic theorems of Dunford–Schwartz and of Chacón–Ornstein. Also a certain amount of effort is spent there in trying to understand what is behind the maximal ergodic theorem of Brunel. This effort leads us to a new proof of this rather striking result. The chapter ends with Chacón's identification of the limit.

The third chapter is concerned with a.e. convergence properties of general orthogonal series. Some classical material, among which are the Kolmogorov inequalities and the martingale theorem, is presented and then the methods used there are extended to give a new proof of the theorem that every orthogonal series can be rearranged to converge a.e. In the process some rather striking combinatorial inequalities are also obtained.

In the fourth and final chapter, after some preliminary material on the Hardy–Littlewood function and the Hilbert transform, we present a proof of L. Carleson's "log log n" result. This is the first result obtained by Carleson in his now-famed investigation.

This chapter may require, if not more maturity, at least more stamina on the part of the reader than the preceding chapters. However, a familiarity with the contents of the fourth chapter should provide adequate foundation for a further study of Carleson's work on the a.e. convergence of Fourier series and the subsequent work of R. Hunt.

These notes do not aspire to be a complete account of almost everywhere convergence results. The basic criterion followed in the selection of the topics has been that the author felt he could at least make a contribution in the exposition of the material, when not in the content.

The proofs of the theorem of Stein, the maximal ergodic inequalities, the theorem of Brunel, and some of Carleson's work should make more palatable reading here than in the original manuscripts. The combinatorial inequalities of Chapter 3 are new and have not appeared in print elsewhere.

We have endeavored to make the contents of these notes accessible to as wide an audience as possible. To this end, here and there we had to include some facts that might appear too elementary or too well known to the expert. In these instances we have tried to compensate by giving the material a new twist, if nothing else. For instance, the first four sections of Chapter 4 could be skipped by readers familiar with Zygmund's treatise on trigonometric series. Indeed, the basic difference in our treatment of the material related to the Hilbert transform lies only in the strictly real variable approach we have adopted throughout.

Also, we have tried to compose the chapters and some of the sections so that they may be read as much as possible independently of each other. Of course, this has been at the expense of some repetitions. We hope that this imperfection will be compensated by the ease with which the material may be read.

During the preparation of these notes several people have contributed remarks and suggestions that have been extremely helpful, and we wish to acknowledge our gratefulness here. These people include S. Sawyer, who helped us with the material in the first chapter; R. V. Chacón and L. Baez-Duarte, in the ergodic theory matters of the second chapter; R. Getoor and E. Bishop, in the martingale portion of the third chapter; L. Carleson, E. Rodemich, and J. Holbrook, in the sections of the third chapter concerned with a.e. convergence properties of orthogonal series; and last, but not least, C. Hadley, who helped us throughout the preparation of these notes.

Finally, we should acknowledge that some of the research presented in this work was carried out under support of AFOSR Grant 1322-67.

A.M.G.

CONTENTS

Preface v

1 SOME BASIC PRINCIPLES 1
- 1.1 Banach's Principle 1
- 1.2 The Estimates of Kolmogorov and Stein 4
- 1.3 Sawyer's Extension 13

2 SOME ERGODIC THEORY 16
- 2.1 Mean Ergodic Theorems 16
- 2.2 Maximal Ergodic Inequalities 22
- 2.3 The Theorem of Dunford and Schwartz 27
- 2.4 The Theorem of Chacón and Ornstein 30
- 2.5 Some Basic Properties of Positive Operators 34
- 2.6 Convergence when $\Phi + T\Phi + \cdots + T^n\Phi \to \infty$ a.e. 38
- 2.7 Brunel's Inequality 42
- 2.8 Convergence and Identification of the Limit in the General Case 49

3 COMBINATORIAL INEQUALITIES AND CONVERGENCE ALMOST EVERYWHERE OF SOME ORTHOGONAL EXPANSIONS 54
- 3.1 Jensen-Type Inequalities 55
- 3.2 Inequalities for Martingales 59
- 3.3 Yet Another Proof of the Martingale Theorem 62
- 3.4 Some Well-Behaved Orthonormal Systems 68
- 3.5 L_p Estimates for Sums of Independent Random Variables 73
- 3.6 Some Combinatorial Inequalities 78
- 3.7 A Proof of the Combinatorial Inequalities 86
- 3.8 Historical Remarks and Further Inequalities 93

4 CARLESON'S "log log *n*" RESULT 98
- 4.1 Preliminaries 98
- 4.2 The Hardy–Littlewood Function 103
- 4.3 Existence and Maximal Estimates for the Hilbert Transform 112
- 4.4 The Exponential Estimate for the Maximal Hilbert Transform 119
- 4.5 Two Lemmas of Carleson 129
- 4.6 Carleson's Fundamental Step 133
- 4.7 The "log log *n*" Estimate 141

References 152

TOPICS in ALMOST EVERYWHERE CONVERGENCE

1

SOME BASIC PRINCIPLES

1.1 BANACH'S PRINCIPLE

In this section we shall try to give an idea of the types of results that must be established in the course of proof of an almost everywhere convergence theorem.

In order not to lose ourselves in a too general setting we shall restrict our study to the case of sequences of linear operators continuous in measure on some L_p space.

To introduce our notation, we describe in detail the elements we shall work with. First, $(\Omega, \mathscr{F}, \mu)$ will be a measure space (which the reader may assume to be of finite measure). We also let B denote $L_p(\Omega, \mathscr{F}, \mu)$ for some fixed $p \geq 1$. In other words, B is the space of all real-valued functions on Ω measurable with respect to $\mathscr{F}$ whose pth power is integrable. Of course, we take as a norm

$$\|f\| = \left(\int_\Omega |f|^p \, d\mu\right)^{1/p}.$$

We shall deal only with linear operators T on B such that

1.1.1 (a) *For every* $f \in B \, |Tf(x)| < \infty$ *a.e. in* Ω.

(b) *T is continuous in measure;* i.e., *if* $f_n, f \in B$, *and* $\|f_n - f\| \to 0$ *as* $n \to \infty$, *then for any* $\epsilon > 0$, $\mu\{x : |Tf_n(x) - Tf(x)| > \epsilon\} \to 0$ *as* $n \to \infty$.

Given a sequence $\{T_n\}$ of such operators we shall set, for every $f \in B$,

$$T^*f(x) = \sup_{n \geq 1} |T_n f(x)|, \qquad T^*_N f(x) = \max_{1 \leq n \leq N} |T_n f(x)|.$$

If we have an almost everywhere convergence result for such a sequence of operators, i.e., if we happen to know that

1.1.2 *For any* $f \in B$ *the sequence* $T_n f(x)$ *is almost everywhere convergent*, then a fortiori we also have that

1.1.3 $$T^*f(x) < \infty \text{ a.e.} \qquad \forall \quad f \in B.$$

The basic fact we are interested in showing is that 1.1.3 itself already implies that the operator T^* must be continuous in measure, uniformly in f. Vice versa, it will also be seen that in most cases such a continuity property for T^* is all that is needed to establish 1.1.2.

The above-mentioned continuity result is expressed in the following

BANACH PRINCIPLE. *If* $T^*f(x) < \infty$ *holds a.e. for all* $f \in B$, *then there is a positive decreasing function* $C(\lambda)$ *defined for* $\lambda > 0$ *and tending to zero as* $\lambda \to \infty$ *such that for all* $f \in B$ *we have*

1.1.4 $$\mu\{x : T^*f(x) > \lambda \|f\|\} \leq C(\lambda) \qquad \forall \quad \lambda > 0.$$

PROOF. Clearly we need only establish 1.1.4 for $\|f\| = 1$. We see that if 1.1.3 holds, then, fixed $\epsilon > 0$, for every $f \in B$ there is an n, possibly depending on f, such that

$$\mu\{x : T^*f(x) > n\} \leq \epsilon.$$

In other words, we have

$$B = \bigcup_{n=1}^{\infty} \{f : \mu\{x : T^*f(x) > n\} \leq \epsilon\}.$$

Now observe that for each n,

1.1.5 $$\{f : \mu\{x : T^*f(x) > n\} \leq \epsilon\}$$

$$= \bigcap_{N=1}^{\infty} \{f : \mu\{x : T_N^*f(x) > n\} \leq \epsilon\}.$$

Note that the operators T_N^* are also continuous in measure; therefore, each of the sets

$$\{f : \mu\{x : T_N^*f(x) > n\} \leq \epsilon\}$$

is closed, and thus so is also the set in 1.1.5. We can then use the Baire category theorem and conclude that one of the sets in 1.1.5

contains a sphere. In other words, for some $f_0 \in B$ and $\delta > 0$ we have

$$\mu\{x : T^*f(x) > n\} \leq \epsilon \qquad \forall \quad \|f - f_0\| \leq \delta.$$

Better yet, we must have

$$\mu\{x : T^*[f_0 + \delta g] > n\} \leq \epsilon \qquad \forall \quad \|g\| \leq 1.$$

Note that since

$$T^*g \leq \frac{1}{\delta} T^*[f_0 + \delta g] + \frac{1}{\delta} T^*f_0,$$

we get

$$\mu\left\{x : T^*g > \frac{2n}{\delta}\right\} \leq \mu\{x : T^*[f_0 + \delta g] > n\} + \mu\{x : T^*f_0 > n\}$$

$$\leq 2\epsilon$$

for all $\|g\| \leq 1$.

This implies that if we set

$$C(\lambda) = \sup_{\|g\| \leq 1} \mu\{x : T^*g > \lambda\},$$

we have

$$\lim_{\lambda \to \infty} C(\lambda) = 0.$$

Thus our assertion is established.

In most cases of interest the almost everywhere convergence of the sequence $T_n f(x)$ can be easily established when f belongs to some special class of functions which is dense in B. When this happens the a.e. convergence of the sequence $T_n f(x)$ for all $f \in B$ is completely equivalent to an inequality of type 1.1.4.

To show this we need only establish the following

THEOREM 1.1.1. *When the operators $\{T_n\}$ satisfy the inequality 1.1.4 the set of functions $f \in B$ for which the sequence $T_n f(x)$ is almost everywhere convergent is closed.*

PROOF. Let this set of functions be denoted by $\mathscr{C}$. We are to show that if for a given $f \in B$ it is true that for every $\epsilon > 0$ there is a $g \in \mathscr{C}$ such that $\|f - g\| < \epsilon$, then $f \in \mathscr{C}$ as well. To this end let us introduce for any $f \in B$ the function

$$R(x, f) = \limsup_{n,m \to \infty} |T_n f(x) - T_m f(x)|.$$

Since $R(x, f) \leq 2T^*(f)$, we have as well

1.1.6 $$\mu\{x : R(x, f) > \lambda \| f \|\} \leq C\left(\frac{\lambda}{2}\right).$$

We see, however, that for any $f \in B$ and any $g \in \mathscr{C}$ we have

$$R(x, f) = R(x, f - g) \qquad \text{for almost all } x,$$

and thus 1.1.6 implies also that

$$\mu\{x : R(x, f) > \lambda \| f - g \|\} \leq C\left(\frac{\lambda}{2}\right).$$

By choosing $\lambda = 1/\epsilon$ and taking $\| f - g \| \leq \epsilon^2$ we get

$$\mu\{x : R(x, f) > \epsilon\} \leq C\left(\frac{1}{2\epsilon}\right).$$

Since ϵ is arbitrary we get that

$$R(x, f) = 0 \quad \text{a.e.}$$

But this is equivalent to the a.e. convergence of $T_n f(x)$.

1.2 THE ESTIMATES OF KOLMOGOROV AND STEIN

The weakness of Banach's principle consists in the fact that nothing is said about the function $C(\lambda)$ except that it tends to zero as $\lambda \to \infty$. However, not much else can be expected as long as we do not require the T_n's to satisfy some additional restrictions.

An inequality considerably more informative than 1.1.4 was obtained by Kolmogorov [25] for the operators associated with the conjugate function integrals. We can describe Kolmogorov's results as follows. We take Ω to be the real line and $\mathscr{F}$ to be the class of Borel sets and $d\mu = dx$. For a function $f(x)$ vanishing outside a finite interval and in $L_1(-\infty, +\infty)$ we set

$$H_n f(x) = \int_{|t| > 1/n} f(x - t)\frac{dt}{t}.\dagger$$

Here set as before

$$H^* f(x) = \sup_{n \geq 1} |H_n f(x)|.$$

† The statement that follows holds even if n is only restricted to be a positive number. However, for the purposes of this exposition we shall assume that it is an integer.

Kolmogorov, using the convergence almost everywhere of the sequence $H_n f(x)$ for all such f, was able to derive an inequality of the form

$$m\{x : H^*f(x) > \lambda\} \leq \frac{C}{\lambda}\int_{-\infty}^{+\infty} |f(x)|\, dx.$$

In other words, he obtained 1.1.4 with $C(\lambda)$ having the special form C/λ.

The crucial property of the operators H_n that makes this result possible is that they all commute with translations; i.e., if we set, for a given α, $E_\alpha f(x) = f(x - \alpha)$, then we see that

$$H_n E_\alpha f = E_\alpha H_n f \qquad \forall \quad n \geq 1,$$

and thus a fortiori

1.2.1 $$H^* E_\alpha = E_\alpha H^*.$$

In the same vein Calderon [43] was able to show that for the partial sums of Fourier series $S_n(x, f)$,† if we set

$$S^*(x, f) = \sup_n |S_n(x, f)|,$$

then the almost everywhere convergence result for all $f \in L_2(-\pi, \pi)$ is equivalent to the statement that

$$m\{x \in [-\pi, \pi] : S^*(x, f) > \lambda\} \leq \frac{C}{\lambda^2}\int_{-\pi}^{\pi} |f|^2\, dx \qquad \forall \quad f \in L_2(-\pi, \pi),$$

in order words, 1.1.4 with $C(\lambda)$ of the form C/λ^2. Again we see that for all translations E_α we have

$$S_n(x, E_\alpha f) = E_\alpha S_n(x, f),$$

and thus also

$$S^*(x, E_\alpha f) = E_\alpha S^*(x, f).$$

Finally, Stein [39] was able to establish a general principle which includes the above two results as special cases. In essence Stein's result states that if Ω is a compact Abelian Lie group, μ is Haar measure, and $\{T_n\}$ is a sequence of operators which commute with translations, then, at least when $1 \leq p \leq 2$, the convergence a.e. of $T_n f(x)$ for all $f \in L_p(\Omega)$ or even only

$$T^* f(x) < \infty \quad \text{a.e.} \qquad \forall \quad f \in L_p(\Omega)$$

† Here we use Zygmund's notation.

implies the inequality

1.2.2 $$\mu\{x : T^*f(x) > \lambda\} \leq \frac{C}{\lambda^p}\int_\Omega |f|^p \, d\mu \qquad \forall \quad f \in L_p(\Omega).$$

Although, as we shall see, there are cases where the same conclusions can still be drawn when $p > 2$, Stein also shows that in general 1.2.2 for $1 \leq p \leq 2$ is the best that can be derived without further hypotheses on the T_n's.

More recently Sawyer and Burkholder extended this principle in independent directions. For further details on these results we refer the reader to the original papers ([37] and [6], [7]).

The basic contribution of Sawyer is to have recognized that a general principle can be derived without a group theoretic setting. All that is needed is that the sequence of operators T_n commutes with a family of measure-preserving transformations of Ω into itself that is large enough to "mix" Ω. This setting permits the formulation of a principle that is broad enough to include also some of the fundamental results of ergodic theory.

This will be the setting that we shall adopt in our presentation. But before proceeding any further we shall give a precise definition of the elements we shall deal with.

As before, we have a measure space $(\Omega, \mathscr{F}, \mu)$ and a sequence of operators $\{T_n\}$ continuous in measure on $B = L_p(\Omega, \mathscr{F}, \mu)$ for some $p \geq 1$. However, now we shall assume that $\mu(\Omega) < \infty$ and that we have, in addition, a family $\mathscr{E}$ of measure-preserving transformations of Ω into itself which is "mixing." By this we mean that given any two sets $A, B \in \mathscr{F}$ of positive measure and any $\alpha > 1$, it is possible to find an element $E \in \mathscr{E}$ such that

1.2.3 $$\mu(\Omega)\mu(A \cap E^{-1}B) \leq \alpha\mu(A)\mu(B).$$

If the transformations of $\mathscr{E}$ commute with each T_n, i.e., if

$$T_nEf = ET_nf\dagger \qquad \forall \quad f \in B, E \in \mathscr{E}, \text{ and } n \geq 1,$$

then we necessarily have

$$T^*Ef = ET^*f \qquad \forall \quad f \in B, \forall \quad E \in \mathscr{E}.$$

We shall, however, only assume that

1.2.4 $$T^*Ef \geq ET^*f \qquad \forall \quad f \in B, \forall \quad E \in \mathscr{E}.$$

† If f is a function defined in Ω and E is a point transformation of Ω into itself, by Ef we mean the function $f(Ex)$.

In fact, there are some applications in which 1.2.4 is the only thing available.

We can now formulate the following

CONTINUITY PRINCIPLE. *Let* $(\Omega, \mathscr{F}, \mu)$ *be a finite measure space,* $\{T_n\}$ *a sequence of linear operators continuous in measure on some space* $B = L_p(\Omega, \mathscr{F}, \mu)(1 \leq p \leq 2)$, *and* $\mathscr{E}$ *some family of measure-preserving transformations of* Ω *into itself. Assume that* $\mathscr{E}$ *is "mixing" in the sense expressed by* 1.2.3 *and that* $\mathscr{E}$ *and* $\{T_n\}$ *"commute" in the sense expressed by* 1.2.4. *Then under these hypotheses, the condition*

$$T^*f(x) < \infty \quad \text{a.e.} \qquad \forall \quad f \in B$$

and the inequality

$$\mu\{x : T^*f(x) > \lambda\} \leq \frac{C}{\lambda^p} \int_\Omega |f|^p \, d\mu \qquad \forall \quad f \in B$$

are equivalent.

PROOF. The methods here will be essentially those used by Stein, but adapted to the present case and simplified somewhat. The main simplification is due to our having put ourselves in a position where we need only work with finite sums.

It will be helpful before getting into details to try to understand the basic ideas behind the arguments. To this end let us explore what we can do to a function $f \in B$ by means of our hypotheses.

Let us set for convenience, for some $\lambda > 0$,

$$A = \{x : T^*f(x) > \lambda\}.$$

If λ is large, we may say that A is a "bad" set for the T^* of f. The hypothesis 1.2.4 essentially means that the T^* of the function $f(Ex)$ is, for a given $E \in \mathscr{E}$, at least as bad as that of the function $f(x)$ is at the transformed point Ex. So if we take transformations $E_1, E_2, \ldots, E_n \in \mathscr{E}$, the functions

$$f_1(x) = f(E_1x), f_2(x) = f(E_2x), \ldots, f_n(x) = f(E_nx)$$

will respectively have a bad T^* at the points of the sets

$$A_1 = E_1^{-1}A, A_2 = E_2^{-1}A, \ldots, A_n = E_n^{-1}A.$$

Hopefully, a function $F(x)$ of the form

1.2.5 $$F(x) = \sum_{\nu=1}^{n} C_\nu f_\nu(x)$$

will have a bad T^* at least on the set

$$A' = \bigcup_{\nu=1}^{n} A_\nu .$$

By making n large and choosing the transformations $E_1, E_2, \ldots, E_n$ adroitly we may try and make $\mu(A')$ quite large. On the other hand, if we take n too large, the norm of F will get out of control. The question is which of these fighting factors will win. It is clear that, if $\mu(A)$ is large to begin with, we might be able to keep $\|F\| \leq 1$ without having to take the C_ν's too small and at the same time succeed in making $\mu(A')$, say, larger than a fixed constant.

If we could carry out this program for arbitrarily large λ, then by Banach's principle we cannot have $T^*f(x) < \infty$ a.e. $\forall\ f \in B$. Thus if T^* has the latter property, we can expect to get a bound for $\mu(A)$.

We shall now make the above arguments more precise and quantitative. Let us recall that we are to keep $\|F\| \leq 1$ and at the same time keep the various terms in 1.2.5 from interfering with each other, so that when $T_m f_{\nu_0}(x)$ is big for some ν_0 and x, then $T_m F(x)$ is also big. On probabilistic grounds it is intuitive that these two goals can be achieved simultaneously if $C_1, C_2, \ldots, C_n$ are chosen "independently." Indeed, as a general rule, a sum of independent terms is never much worse or much better than each individual term. This observation makes it plausible that we should set

$$C_\nu = \frac{1}{M}\Phi_\nu(\omega)$$

where M is a constant to be determined and $\Phi_1(\omega), \Phi_2(\omega), \ldots, \Phi_n(\omega)$ are the first n Rademacher functions.† This gives us an analytic way to represent the 2^n functions

$$\frac{1}{M}(\pm f_1 + f_2 \pm \cdots \pm f_n).$$

So we shall set

$$F(x, \omega) = \frac{1}{M}\sum_{\nu=1}^{n} \Phi_\nu(\omega) f_\nu(x).$$

† See Section 3.4 for the definition and basic properties of the Rademacher system.

Let us first estimate the norm of $F(x, \omega)$. Note that by Holder's inequality, assuming $p \leq 2$,

$$\int_0^1 |F(x, \omega)|^p \, d\omega \leq \left(\int_0^1 |F(x, \omega)|^2 \, d\omega \right)^{p/2}.$$

By the orthogonality of the Rademacher function, this gives

$$\int_0^1 |F(x, \omega)|^p \, d\omega \leq \left(\frac{1}{M^2} \sum_{\nu=1}^{n} [f_\nu(x)]^2 \right)^{p/2}.$$

Using the inequality

$$\left(\sum_{\nu=1}^{n} p_\nu^\alpha \right)^{1/\alpha} \leq \left(\sum_{\nu=1}^{n} p_\nu^\beta \right)^{1/\beta},$$

(valid when $p_1, p_2, \ldots, p_n \geq 0$ and $\alpha \geq \beta$), we get

$$\int_0^1 |F(x, \omega)|^p \, d\omega \leq \frac{1}{M^p} \sum_{\nu=1}^{n} |f_\nu(x)|^p.$$

Integrating over Ω and applying Fubini's theorem we finally obtain

$$\int_0^1 \int_\Omega |F(x, \omega)|^p \, d\mu \, d\omega \leq \frac{1}{M^p} n \int_\Omega |f(\omega)|^p \, d\mu.$$

Assume for convenience that $\|f\| \leq 1$. We see then that

1.2.6 $$m\left\{ \omega : \int_\Omega |F(x, \omega)|^p \, d\mu > 1 \right\} \leq \frac{n}{M^p}.$$

We deduce that if $M^p > n$, we shall have plenty of ω's for which the function $F(x, \omega)$ has norm less than or equal to one.

Suppose now that $x \in A' = \bigcup_{\nu=1}^{n} A_\nu$. This means that $x \in A_{\nu_0}$ for some ν_0. In view of the definition of the A_ν's, this means that the point $y = E_{\nu_0} x$ belongs to A. Therefore, by 1.2.4, we get

$$T^* f_{\nu_0}(x) = T^* E_{\nu_0} f(x) \geq E_{\nu_0} T^* f(x) = T^* f(y) > \lambda.$$

This implies that for some m

$$T_m f_{\nu_0}(x) > \lambda.$$

Note that for each ω,

$$T_m F(x, \omega) = \frac{1}{M} \sum_{\nu=1}^{n} \varphi_\nu(\omega) T_m f_\nu(x).$$

Finally, observe that the quantity

$$\frac{1}{M}\sum_{\nu\neq\nu_0}\varphi_\nu(\omega)T_m f_\nu(x)$$

may or may not have the same sign as the term $(1/M)\varphi_{\nu_0}(\omega)f_{\nu_0}(x)$; however, that quantity is either zero, or for each ω for which it does not have the same sign as this term there is an ω' for which it does. More precisely, we infer that for each $x \in A'$ there is a set $I(x)$ of points ω such that

1.2.7 (a) $m(I(x)) \geq \frac{1}{2}$;

(b) For $\omega \in I(x)$, $T^*F(x,\omega) > \dfrac{\lambda}{M}$.

Now let us see how large we can make the measure of A'. To this end it will be convenient to assume, since there is no loss, that $\mu(\Omega) = 1$. Set also

$$B = {}^cA, \qquad B_\nu = {}^cA_\nu = E_\nu^{-1}B.†$$

For a given n, by 1.2.3, we can find $E_1, E_2,\ldots, E_n \in \mathscr{E}$ so that

$$\mu(B_1 \cap B_2 \cap \cdots \cap B_n) \leq \frac{e}{2}(1-\mu(A))^n.$$

Since ${}^cA' = \bigcap_{\nu=1}^n B_\nu$,

$$\mu(A') = 1 - \mu\left(\bigcap_{\nu=1}^{n} B_\nu\right) \geq 1 - \frac{e}{2}(1-\mu(A))^n.$$

Using the inequality $1 - x \leq e^{-x}$ we get

$$\mu(A') \geq 1 - \frac{e}{2}e^{-n\mu(A)}.$$

And so, for such a choice of $E_1, E_2,\ldots, E_n$, we have

1.2.8 $$\mu(A') \geq \tfrac{1}{2},$$

as soon as

1.2.9 $$n\mu(A) \geq 1.$$

† ${}^cA$ = complement of A, etc.

Our goal is now to pick ω in such a way that

$$\|F(x,\omega)\| = \left(\int_\Omega |F(x,\omega)|^p \, d\mu\right)^{1/p} \le 1,$$

and at the same time succeed in getting

$$\mu\left\{x : T^*F(x,\omega) > \frac{\lambda}{M}\right\}$$

to be as large as possible. Let

$$\Gamma = \{\omega : \|F(x,\omega)\| \le 1\};$$

then, according to 1.2.6,

$$m(\Gamma) \ge 1 - \frac{n}{M^p} \ge \tfrac{3}{4},$$

provided that

1.2.10 $$M^p \ge 4n.$$

Combing the lower bound on $m(\Gamma)$ with 1.2.7(a) we obtain

1.2.11 $$m(I(x) \cap \Gamma) \ge \tfrac{1}{4} \qquad \forall \quad x \in A'.$$

Let us now set

$$\chi(x,\omega) = \begin{cases} 1 & \text{if } T^*F(x,\omega) \ge \dfrac{\lambda}{M}, \\ 0 & \text{otherwise.} \end{cases}$$

Our estimate in 1.2.11 and 1.2.7(b) tells us that

$$\int_\Gamma \chi(x,\omega)\, d\omega \ge \tfrac{1}{4}$$

and thus also, in view of 1.2.8,

$$\int_{A'} \int_\Gamma \chi(x,\omega)\, d\omega \, d\mu \ge \tfrac{1}{8}.$$

By Fubini's theorem this implies that there must be an $\omega \in \Gamma$ such that

$$\int_{A'} \chi(x,\omega)\, d\mu \ge \tfrac{1}{8}.$$

Recapitulating our results, we see that if 1.2.9 and 1.2.10 hold, i.e., if we simultaneously have

$$n\mu(A) \geq 1 \qquad \text{and} \qquad M^p \geq 4n,$$

then there is an ω such that

$$\text{(a)} \ \mu\left\{x : T^*F(x, \omega) > \frac{\lambda}{M}\right\} \geq \tfrac{1}{8};$$

$$\text{(b)} \int_\Omega |F(x, \omega)|^p \, d\mu \leq 1.$$

Now, under the assumption that $T^*f(x) < \infty$ a.e. $\forall f \in B$, using Banach's principle, we deduce that there must be a constant C such that if

$$\frac{\lambda}{M} \geq C$$

then (when $\omega \in \Gamma$)

$$\mu\left\{x : T^*F(x, \omega) > \frac{\lambda}{M}\right\} < \tfrac{1}{8}.$$

Since n and M are at our disposal we can certainly take

$$M = \frac{\lambda}{C}$$

and

$$n = \left[\frac{M^p}{4}\right] = \left[\frac{\lambda^p}{4C^p}\right].$$

In order to avoid contradiction we must conclude that

$$\mu(A) < \frac{1}{n} = \frac{1}{[\lambda^p/4C^p]} \leq \frac{8C^p}{\lambda^p},$$

at least when $\lambda^p \geq 8C^p$. For small λ, of course, we have

$$\mu(A) \leq 1,$$

so our proof is complete.

1.3 SAWYER'S EXTENSION

Sawyer observed that Stein's theorem remains valid when $p > 2$ in the case that the operators T_n are assumed to be positive. By this we mean that for each n,

$$f \geq 0 \text{ a.e.} \Rightarrow T_n f \geq 0 \text{ a.e.}$$

We thus have the following

CONTINUITY PRINCIPLE FOR POSITIVE OPERATORS. *Let $(\Omega, \mathscr{F}, \mu)$ be a finite measure space, $\{T_n\}$ a sequence of positive linear operators continuous in measure on some space $L_p = B(1 \leq p < \infty)$, and $\mathscr{E}$ some family of measure-preserving transformations of Ω into itself. Assume that $\mathscr{E}$ is "mixing" in the sense expressed by* 1.2.3 *and that $\mathscr{E}$ and $\{T_n\}$ "commute" in the sense expressed by* 1.2.4; *then under these hypotheses the condition*

$$T^*f(x) < \infty \quad \text{a.e.} \qquad \forall \quad f \in B$$

and the inequality

1.3.1 $$\mu\{x : T^*f(x) > \lambda\} \leq \frac{C}{\lambda^p} \int_\Omega |f|^p \, d\mu \qquad \forall \quad f \in B$$

are equivalent.

PROOF. This result is much easier to establish. As before, we take $E_1, E_2, \ldots, E_n \in \mathscr{E}$ and let, for a given nonnegative $f \in B$,

$$f_v(x) = f(E_v x).$$

However, now we can set

$$F(x) = \frac{1}{M} \max_{1 \leq v \leq n} f_v(x).$$

In fact, by the positivity of T_n, automatically we have

$$T_n F(x) \geq \frac{1}{M} T_n f_v(x) \qquad v = 1, 2, \ldots, n.$$

Thus

$$T^*F(x) \geq \frac{1}{M} \max_{1 \leq v \leq n} T^*f_v(x).$$

So if $A = \{x : T^*f(x) > \lambda\}$ and $A_v = E_v^{-1}A$, we immediately get that

$$\mu\left\{x : T^*F(x) > \frac{\lambda}{M}\right\} \geq \mu\left\{\max_{1 \leq \nu \leq n} T^*f_\nu(x) > \lambda\right\} \geq \mu\left\{\bigcup_{\nu=1}^{n} A_\nu\right\}.$$

We have seen that by an adroit choice of $E_1, E_2, \ldots, E_n$ we can make

$$\mu\left\{\bigcup_{\nu=1}^{n} A_\nu\right\} \geq \tfrac{1}{2},$$

provided

1.3.2 $$n\mu(A) \geq 1.$$

On the other hand, we see that

$$|F(x)|^p \leq \frac{1}{M^p} \sum_{\nu=1}^{n} |f_\nu(x)|^p.$$

Thus, if $\int_\Omega |f(x)|^p \, d\mu \leq 1$,

$$\int_\Omega |F(x)|^p \, d\mu \leq \frac{n}{M^p} \leq 1,$$

provided

1.3.3 $$n \leq M^p.$$

Now the proof can proceed as before. By Banach's theorem, if $T^*f(x) < \infty \; \forall \; f \in B$, we must have a constant C such that

$$\mu\left\{x : T^*f(x) > \frac{\lambda}{M}\right\} < \tfrac{1}{2}$$

as soon as 1.3.3 holds and

$$\frac{\lambda}{M} \geq C.$$

Since we are free to take $M = \lambda/C$ and $n = [\lambda^p/C^p]$, 1.3.2 cannot hold and thus we get an estimate of the form

1.3.4 $$\mu\{x : T^*f(x) > \lambda\} \leq \frac{C}{\lambda^p} \int_\Omega |f|^p \, d\mu$$

for all nonnegative f. To complete the proof we need to establish the same inequality for general f. However, this follows immediately.

Indeed, the positivity of each T_n implies

$$T_n|f| \geq |T_n f| \qquad \forall \quad n, f \in B,$$

and thus

$$T^*|f| \geq T^*f \qquad \forall \quad f \in B.$$

Consequently, for any $\lambda > 0$ we have

$$\mu\{x : T^*f > \lambda\} \leq \mu\{x : T^*|f| > \lambda\}.$$

Our proof is thus complete.

The above principle has wider applicability than it may seem on the surface. In fact, although the operators T_n themselves may not be positive, it may happen that they are of the form $T_n = P_n T$, where the P_n's are positive and T is some linear operator bounded in L_p. Then, if we have an estimate of type 1.3.1 for P^*, we will automatically obtain one for T^*. This can be done, for instance, in the case of the conjugate function integrals.

2

SOME ERGODIC THEORY

2.1 MEAN ERGODIC THEOREMS

We shall work here with a measure space $(\Omega, \mathscr{F}, \mu)$, of possibly infinite measure, and a linear operator T defined in $L_1(\Omega, \mathscr{F}, \mu)$ such that

(1) $f \geq 0$ a.e. $\Rightarrow Tf \geq 0$ a.e.;

(2) $\int_\Omega |Tf| \, d\mu \leq \int_\Omega |f| \, d\mu.$

Sometimes we shall also require T to satisfy the condition that for all $C > 0$,

(3) $|f| \leq C$ a.e. $\Rightarrow |Tf| \leq C$ a.e.

Our main object of study here will be the almost everywhere convergence behavior of the ratios

2.1.1 $$R_n(f) = \frac{f + Tf + \cdots + T^n f}{n + 1}$$

as $n \to \infty$.

The classical result of G. D. Birkhoff states that in case $\mu(\Omega) < \infty$ and $Tf(x) = f(Ex)$, where E is a measure-preserving transformation of Ω into itself, then $R_n(f)$ is almost everywhere convergent as $n \to \infty$ for all $f \in L_1$. The result of E. Hopf, which is also classical now, asserts that the same is true when $\mu(\Omega) < \infty$ and T in addition to (1) and (2) satisfies instead of (3) the condition

(3′) $T1 = 1.$

It is easily seen that (1) and (3′) imply (3). Thus we shall be working in a setup that includes both the results of Birkhoff and Hopf. Indeed, at the end of this section we shall consider also the cases in which (1) is not assumed at all, and we shall obtain the ergodic theorem of Dunford and Schwartz. However, before getting into these matters we need to establish a few fundamental properties of such an operator T. We shall present these in the form of separate propositions.

PROPOSITION 2.1.1. *If* $f_1, f_2, \ldots, f_n \in L_1$, *then*

2.1.2 $$\max_{1 \le \nu \le n} Tf_\nu \le T \max_{1 \le \nu \le n} f_\nu .$$

PROOF. Since

$$f_\nu \le \max_{1 \le \mu \le n} f_\mu$$

by the linearity of T and (1) we get

$$Tf_\nu \le T \max_{1 \le \mu \le n} f_\mu .$$

Taking the maximum with respect to ν, 2.1.2 follows.

PROPOSITION 2.1.2. *If* $|f_n| \le F$ *with* $F \in L_1$ *and* $f_n \to f$ a.e., *then*

$$Tf_n \to Tf \text{ a.e.}$$

PROOF. We can clearly assume $f = 0$. Set $g_n = \sup_{m \ge n} |f_m|$. Then by our assumptions we have

2.1.3 (a) $g_n \downarrow 0$ a.e.;

(b) $g_n \le F \in L_1$.

Since the sequence Tg_n is monotone, if Tg_n fails to converge to zero a.e., then for some $\epsilon > 0$ we have

$$\mu\{\inf Tg_n > \epsilon\} = \theta > 0.$$

Thus, by (2),

$$0 < \epsilon\theta \le \int_\Omega Tg_n \, d\mu \le \int_\Omega g_n \, d\mu \qquad \forall \quad n.$$

However, in view of 2.1.3, this inequality yields a contradiction when $n \to \infty$.

PROPOSITION 2.1.3. *If T in addition to* (1) *and* (2) *satisfies* (3), *then for any constant $C > 0$ and any $g \in L_1$ we have*

2.1.4 $$(Tg - C)^+ \leq T(g - C)^+.\dagger$$

PROOF. Set

$$g_C = \begin{Bmatrix} C \text{ when } g > C \\ -C \text{ when } g < -C \\ g \text{ when } |g| \leq C \end{Bmatrix}, \qquad R_C = g - g_C.$$

It is easily seen that in any case

$$R_C \leq (g - C)^+.$$

Thus using (1) and (3) we get

$$Tg = Tg_C + TR_C \leq C + T(g - C)^+,$$

and 2.1.4 clearly follows by the positivity of $T(g - C)^+$.

PROPOSITION 2.1.4. *If T satisfies* (1), (2), *and* (3), *then for any $g \in L_1 \cap L_\infty$ and any $p > 1$ the function Tg is in L_p and*

2.1.5 $$\int_\Omega |Tg|^p \, d\mu \leq \int_\Omega |g|^p \, d\mu.$$

Thus such a T always admits a unique extension to a linear operator of L_p into itself for every $p > 1$.

PROOF. This result is usually obtained by means of the M. Riesz interpolation theorem. However, we shall see that there is no need here to use such a sophisticated tool.

First, we notice that since $|Tg| \leq T|g|$, we need only show 2.1.5 for $g \geq 0$. Our point of departure will be the inequality 2.1.4, which we integrate over Ω and obtain by means of (2):

$$\int_\Omega (Tg - C)^+ \, d\mu \leq \int_\Omega T(g - C)^+ \, d\mu \leq \int_\Omega (g - C)^+ \, d\mu.$$

It is worthwhile writing this relation in the form

2.1.6 $$\int_\Omega (Tg - C)\chi(Tg, C) \, d\mu \leq \int_\Omega (g - C)\chi(g, C) \, d\mu$$

† By $(x)^+$ we mean $\max[0, x]$; we also set $(x)^- = \max[0, -x]$.

with

$$\chi(u, C) = \begin{cases} 1 & \text{if } u > C, \\ 0 & \text{if } u \leq C. \end{cases}$$

If we multiply the right-hand side of 2.1.6 by C^{p-2} (for a $p > 1$) and integrate with respect to C from 0 to ∞ we obtain, by Fubini's theorem,

$$\int_0^\infty C^{p-2} \int_\Omega (g - C)\chi(g, C)\, d\mu\, dC = \left(\frac{1}{p-1} - \frac{1}{p}\right) \int_\Omega g^p\, d\mu < \infty.$$

Since the integrands are nonnegative, the left-hand side of 2.1.6 can also be so integrated. Thus, again by Fubini's theorem, we obtain

$$\left(\frac{1}{p-1} - \frac{1}{p}\right) \int_\Omega |Tg|^p\, d\mu \leq \left(\frac{1}{p-1} - \frac{1}{p}\right) \int_\Omega |g|^p\, d\mu.$$

This establishes 2.1.5.

Here and in the following an operator T satisfying (1), (2), and (3) will be assumed defined on each L_p ($p \geq 1$) and satisfying 2.1.5.

PROPOSITION 2.1.5. *Under the assumptions* (1), (2), *and* (3) *we can define an operator P having also these same properties and such that for any $p > 1$,*

2.1.7 $$\lim_{n\to\infty} \left\| \frac{f + \cdots + T^n f}{n+1} - Pf \right\|_p = 0 \qquad \forall\ f \in L_p.$$

Consequently, P must also satisfy the relation

2.1.8 $$TP = P.$$

PROOF. This result, which is usually referred to as the mean ergodic theorem, is often obtained for $p = 2$ by Hilbert space techniques. We shall establish it here by a little known method due to F. Riesz.

The basic step is the following

THEOREM 2.1.1. *Let T be a linear operator from L_p to L_p (for a fixed $p > 1$) which is only assumed to satisfy*

2.1.9 $$\int_\Omega |Tf|^p\, d\mu \leq \int_\Omega |f|^p\, d\mu \qquad \forall\ f \in L_p.$$

Then for every $f \in L_p$ the ratios

$$R_n(f) = \frac{f + Tf + \cdots + T^n f}{n+1}$$

form a Cauchy sequence in the mean. Consequently, if we denote by Pf the limit function, it is easily verified that the operator P is linear and satisfies

(a) $f \geq 0 \Rightarrow Pf \geq 0$ (if the same is true for T);

2.1.10 (b) $\int_\Omega |Pf|^p \, d\mu \leq \int_\Omega |f|^p \, d\mu$;

(c) $|f| \leq C \Rightarrow |Pf| \leq C$ (if the same is true for T).

PROOF. Set

$$\mu_N = \inf_{\substack{\lambda_0 + \lambda_1 + \cdots + \lambda_N = 1 \\ \lambda_i \geq 0}} \|\lambda_0 f + \cdots + \lambda_N T^N f\|_p, \qquad \mu = \inf_N \mu_N.$$

The crucial observation is that for all $f \in L_p$,

2.1.11 $$\lim_{n \to \infty} \|R_n(f)\|_p = \mu.$$

In fact, let

$$g = \lambda_0 f + \cdots + \lambda_N T^N f \qquad (\lambda_i \geq 0, \lambda_0 + \cdots + \lambda_N = 1)$$

be such that

$$\|g\|_p \leq \mu + \epsilon.$$

Then since

$$\frac{g + Tg + \cdots + T^n g}{n+1} = \lambda_0 \frac{f + \cdots + T^n f}{n+1} + \lambda_1 \frac{Tf + \cdots + T^{n+1} f}{n+1} + \cdots + \lambda_N \frac{T^N f + \cdots + T^{n+N} f}{n+1},$$

we get

$$\|R_n(g) - R_n(f)\|_p \leq \sum_{\nu=1}^{N} \lambda_\nu \frac{\|f\|_p + \cdots + \|T^{\nu-1} f\|_p + \|T^{n+1} f\|_p + \cdots + \|T^{n+\nu} f\|_p}{n+1} \leq \frac{2N\|f\|_p}{n+1}.$$

Thus

$$\mu \leq \|R_n(f)\|_p \leq \|R_n(f) - R_n(g)\|_p + \|R_n(g)\|_p \leq \frac{2N\|f\|_p}{n+1} + \mu + \epsilon.$$

This clearly implies 2.1.11.

For $p = 2$ the convergence of the $R_n(f)$'s then follows immediately from the parallelogram inequality,

$$\|R_n(f) - R_m(f)\|_2^2 + \|R_n(f) + R_m(f)\|_2^2 \leq 2\|R_n(f)\|_2^2 + 2\|R_n(f)\|_2^2.$$

In fact, from the definition of μ this gives

$$\|R_n(f) - R_m(f)\|_2^2 \leq 2[\|R_n(f)\|_2^2 - \mu^2] + 2[\|R_m(f)\|_2^2 - \mu^2].$$

For $p \neq 2$ a slightly less simple inequality has to be used:

2.1.12 $$\int_\Omega |f_1 - f_2|^p \, d\mu \leq C_p \left[\int_\Omega |f_1|^p + \int_\Omega |f_2|^p - 2\int_\Omega \left| \frac{f_1 + f_2}{2} \right|^p \right]^{\min[1, p/2]},\dagger$$

where C_p is a constant depending only on p and $\int_\Omega |f_1|^p, \int_\Omega |f_2|^p$ are to be less than or equal to one.

To complete the proof of Proposition 2.1.5, observe that if $f \in L_1 \cap L_\infty$, then of course $f \in L_2$ and

$$\left\| \frac{f + Tf + \cdots + T^n f}{n+1} - Pf \right\|_2 \to 0 \qquad \text{as} \quad n \to \infty.$$

Thus for every set E of finite measure we deduce that

$$\lim_{n \to \infty} \int_E \frac{f + \cdots + T^n f}{n+1} \, d\mu = \int_E Pf \, d\mu.$$

Consequently, for all such E,

$$\int_E Pf \leq \int_\Omega f \qquad \forall \quad f \geq 0.$$

In other words, since $|Pf| \leq P|f|$, when T satisfies (1),

$$\int |Pf| \leq \int |f| \qquad \forall \quad f \in L_1 \cap L_\infty.$$

† This can be established by expressing

$$|f_1|^p + |f_2|^p - 2\left|\frac{f_1 + f_2}{2}\right|^p$$

as an integral involving the second derivative of $|x|^p$. The constant C_p tends to infinity as $p \to 1$.

This means that the definition of P can be extended to all of L_1 as well, so as to satisfy the latter inequality for all $f \in L_1$.

2.2 MAXIMAL ERGODIC INEQUALITIES

As suggested by the continuity principle, we might expect, if the ratios

$$R_n(f) = \frac{f + Tf + \cdots + T^n f}{n + 1}$$

are almost everywhere convergent for every $f \in L_1$, that there is an inequality of the type

2.2.1 $$\mu\{x : R^*(f) > \lambda\} \leq \frac{C}{\lambda} \int_\Omega |f|\, d\mu \qquad \forall \quad f \in L_1,$$

where we have, of course, set

$$R^*(f) = \sup_{n \geq 0} \left| \frac{f + Tf + \cdots + T^n f}{n + 1} \right|.$$

This is indeed what we are going to show in this section. To this end let us introduce some notation. We shall at first assume only that T satisfies (1) and (2). This given, for every $f \in L_1$, set

$$E^n(f) = \{x : \max_{0 \leq v \leq n} (f + Tf + \cdots + T^n f) > 0\},$$

$$E(f) = \{x : \sup_{0 \leq v} (f + Tf + \cdots + T^v f) > 0\}.$$

Clearly, as $n \to \infty$

$$E^n(f) \uparrow E(f).$$

It will also be convenient to introduce the function

$$\varphi_n(x_1, x_2, \ldots, x_n) = \max_{1 \leq v \leq n} (x_1 + x_2 + \cdots + x_n)^+.$$

We see then that

2.2.2 $$E^n(f) = \{x : \varphi_n(f, Tf, \ldots, T^n f) > 0\}.$$

We observe that the function φ_n has the following property: Whenever $\varphi_n(x_1, x_2, \ldots, x_n) > 0$, then no matter what is the value of x_{n+1} we have

2.2.3 $$x_1 + \varphi_n(x_2, x_3, \ldots, x_{n+1}) \geq \varphi_n(x_1, x_2, \ldots, x_n).$$

This is easily verified. In fact, in any case

$$x_1 + \varphi_n(x_2, x_3, \ldots, x_{n+1}) \geq \max_{1 \leq \nu \leq n} (x_1 + x_2 + \cdots + x_\nu).$$

However, when $\varphi_n(x_1, x_2, \ldots, x_n) > 0$ we also have

$$\varphi_n(x_1, x_2, \ldots, x_n) = \max_{1 \leq \nu \leq n} (x_1 + x_2 + \cdots + x_\nu).$$

We are now in a position to prove the

HOPF MAXIMAL ERGODIC THEOREM 2.2.1. *If T satisfies (1) and (2), then $\forall f \in L_1$,*

$$\int_{E_n(f)} f \geq 0.$$

Consequently, letting $n \to \infty$ we also have

2.2.4 $$\int_{E(f)} f \geq 0 \qquad \forall \quad f \in L_1.$$

PROOF. In view of 2.2.2 and 2.2.3 we get

2.2.5 $$\int_{E^n(f)} f \geq \int_{E^n(f)} [\varphi_n(f, \ldots, T^n f) - \varphi_n(Tf, \ldots, T^{n+1} f)] \, d\mu.$$

Using property (1) (and Proposition 2.1.1),

$$\begin{aligned}\varphi_n(Tf, \ldots, T^{n+1} f) &= \max_{0 \leq \nu \leq n} (Tf + \cdots + T^{\nu+1} f)^+ \\ &\leq \max_{0 \leq \nu \leq n} T(f + \cdots + T^\nu f)^+ \\ &\leq T \max_{0 \leq \nu \leq n} (f + \cdots + T^\nu f)^+ = T\varphi_n(f, \ldots, T^n f).\end{aligned}$$

Substituting in 2.2.5, and using the fact that $\varphi_n \geq 0$,

$$\begin{aligned}\int_{E^n(f)} f &\geq \int_{E^n(f)} [\varphi_n(f, \ldots, T^n f) - T\varphi_n(f, \ldots, T^n f)] \, d\mu \\ &\geq \int_\Omega [\varphi_n(f, \ldots, T^n f) - T\varphi_n(f, \ldots, T^n f)] \, d\mu \\ &\geq 0.\end{aligned}$$

The result now follows from property (2).

Let us now introduce the sets

$$E_\lambda^n(f) = \{\max_{0 \le \nu \le n} R_\nu(f) > \lambda\}, \qquad E_\lambda(f) = \{\sup_{\nu \ge 0} R_\nu(f) > \lambda\}.$$

We see that when $\mu(\Omega) < \infty$ and $T1 = 1$, then

$$E_\lambda^n(f) = E^n(f - \lambda).$$

[Indeed, $R_\nu(f) > \lambda \Leftrightarrow f + \cdots + T^\nu f - (\nu + 1)\lambda = (f - \lambda) + \cdots + T^\nu(f - \lambda) > 0$.] Thus for such a T (by 2.2.4) we must have

2.2.6 $$\int_{E_\lambda(f)} (f - \lambda) \ge 0.$$

This relation is easily seen to give 2.2.1. The remarkable fact is that this same relation holds even under the sole assumptions (1), (2), and (3). Indeed, we have

THEOREM 2.2.2. *If T satisfies* (1), (2), *and* (3), *then for all $f \in L_p$* ($p \ge 1$) *and all $\lambda > 0$ we have*

2.2.7 (a) $\mu\{E_\lambda^n(f)\} < \infty$;

(b) $$\int_{E_\lambda^n(f)} (f - \lambda) \ge 0 \qquad \forall \quad n \ge 0.$$

In particular, when $f \in L_1$, we obtain, letting $n \to \infty$,

2.2.8 $$\mu\{E_\lambda(f)\} \le \frac{1}{\lambda} \int_\Omega |f| \, d\mu.$$

PROOF. It is clear from the definition of $E_\lambda^n(f)$ that

$$E_\lambda^n(f) = \{\varphi_n(f - \lambda, \dots, T^n f - \lambda) > 0\}.$$

But, when $\varphi_n(f - \lambda, \dots, T^n f - \lambda) > 0$, at least one of the inequalities $T^\nu f > \lambda$ must hold. Thus, if $f \in L_p$, we deduce

$$\mu\{E_\lambda^n(f)\} \le \sum_{\nu=0}^{n} \mu\{|T^\nu f| > \lambda\} \le \frac{1}{\lambda^p} \sum_{\nu=0}^{n} \int_\Omega |T^\nu f|^p \, d\mu < \infty.$$

This proves 2.2.7(a). Thus, as before, we can start with

$$\int_{E_\lambda^n(f)} (f - \lambda) \ge \int_{E_\lambda^n(f)} \{\varphi_n(f - \lambda, \dots, T^n f - \lambda) - \varphi_n(Tf - \lambda, \dots, T^{n+1} f - \lambda)\} \, d\mu.$$

However, now, using Proposition 2.1.3 with $C = (\nu + 1)\lambda$, $g = f + \cdots + T^{\nu} f$, we get

$$[Tf + \cdots + T^{\nu+1} f - (\nu + 1)\lambda]^+ \leq T[f + \cdots + T^{\nu} f - (\nu + 1)\lambda]^+.$$

Thus again we have

$$\varphi_n(Tf - \lambda, \ldots, T^{n+1} f - \lambda) \leq T\varphi_n(f - \lambda, \ldots, T^n f - \lambda).$$

This gives, as before,

$$\int_{E^n(f)} (f - \lambda)\, d\mu \geq \int_{\Omega} [\varphi_n(f - \lambda, \ldots, T^n f - \lambda) - T\varphi_n(f - \lambda, \ldots, T^n f - \lambda)]\, d\mu \geq 0,$$

and the theorem is established.

The process of replacing 2.2.7 by 2.2.8 is wasteful. Indeed, although this is often not realized, 2.2.7 has considerably more content than 2.2.8. It will be rewarding to make a more efficient use of 2.2.7. The basic idea here apparently goes back to *N*. Wiener and can be expressed by the following

STRONG ESTIMATE THEOREM 2.2.3. *Let X and Y be two nonnegative measurable functions and assume that $X \in L_p$ for some $p > 1$. Further, suppose that for each $\lambda > 0$ we have*

2.2.9 (a) $\mu\{Y > \lambda\} < \infty$;

(b) $\mu\{Y > \lambda\} \leq \dfrac{1}{\lambda} \displaystyle\int_{\{Y > \lambda\}} X\, d\mu.$

Then Y must necessarily be also in L_p and

2.2.10 $$\int_{\Omega} Y^p\, d\mu \leq \left(\frac{p}{p-1}\right)^p \int_{\Omega} X^p\, d\mu.$$

PROOF. Let us first assume that Y itself is also in L_p. This given, we write the inequality 2.2.9(b) in the form

2.2.11 $$\lambda \int_{\Omega} \chi(Y, \lambda)\, d\mu \leq \int_{\Omega} \chi(Y, \lambda) \chi\, d\mu,$$

where we have set as before

$$\chi(u, \lambda) = \begin{cases} 1 & \text{when } u > \lambda, \\ 0 & \text{when } 0 \leq u \leq \lambda. \end{cases}$$

We then multiply both sides of 2.2.11 by λ^{p-2} and integrate with respect to λ from 0 to ∞ to obtain, by Fubini's theorem and Hölder's inequality,

$$\frac{1}{p}\int_\Omega Y^p\,d\mu \le \frac{1}{p-1}\int_\Omega X Y^{p-1}\,d\mu$$
$$\le \frac{1}{p-1}\left[\int_\Omega X^p\,d\mu\right]^{1/p}\left[\int_\Omega Y^p\,d\mu\right]^{(p-1)/p}.$$

This clearly implies 2.2.10, at least when $Y \in L_p$.

To establish the result in full generality, observe that, for any given $C > 0$, the function

$$Y_C = \begin{cases} Y & \text{when } Y < C, \\ C & \text{when } Y \ge C, \end{cases}$$

satisfies also the inequality

$$\mu\{Y_C > \lambda\} \le \frac{1}{\lambda}\int_{\{Y_C > \lambda\}} X\,d\mu.\dagger$$

In case $\mu(\Omega) < \infty$, Y_C will be in L_p and thus by the above argument it must satisfy

$$\int_\Omega Y_C^p\,d\mu \le \left(\frac{p}{p-1}\right)^p \int_\Omega X^p\,d\mu.$$

Thus the result for Y can be obtained by letting $C \to \infty$. In case $\mu(\Omega) = \infty$, the above observation at least shows that we can assume without loss that Y is bounded. Let, then, $0 \le Y \le C$ and set for convenience $Z_\epsilon = (Y - \epsilon)^+$. We see then [by 2.2.9(a)] that

$$\mu\{Z_\epsilon > 0\} = \mu\{Y > \epsilon\} < \infty$$

and thus, since $0 \le Z_\epsilon \le C$, Z_ϵ must be in L_p. Now note that, by 2.2.9(b), for all $\lambda > 0$ we have

$$\mu\{Z_\epsilon > \lambda\} = \mu\{Y > \lambda + \epsilon\} \le \frac{1}{\lambda + \epsilon}\int_{\{Y > \lambda + \epsilon\}} X\,d\mu$$
$$\le \frac{1}{\lambda}\int_{\{Z_\epsilon > \lambda\}} X\,d\mu.$$

† When $\lambda \ge C$, $\mu\{Y_C > \lambda\} = 0$, and when $\lambda < C$, the sets $\{Y_C > \lambda\}$ and $\{Y > \lambda\}$ are the same.

Therefore, we deduce that

$$\int_\Omega Z_\epsilon^p \, d\mu \leq \left(\frac{p}{p-1}\right)^p \int_\Omega X^p \, d\mu.$$

The result for Y is then obtained by letting $\epsilon \to 0$. This completes the proof of the theorem.

By combining the results of Theorems 2.2.2 and 2.2.3 we can deduce the following

COROLLARY 2.2.1. *If T satisfies (1), (2), and (3) and $f \in L_p$ $(p > 1)$, then*

2.2.12 $$\int_\Omega [R^*(f)]^p \, d\mu \leq \left(\frac{p}{p-1}\right)^p \int_\Omega |f|^p \, d\mu.$$

PROOF. Setting

$$R_n^*(f) = \max_{0 \leq \nu \leq n} \left| \frac{f + \cdots + T^\nu f}{\nu + 1} \right|,$$

Theorem 2.2.2 tells us that for each $\lambda > 0$,

(a) $\mu\{R_n^*(f) > \lambda\} < \infty$;

(b) $\mu\{R_n^*(f) > \lambda\} \leq \dfrac{1}{\lambda} \displaystyle\int_{\{R_n^*(f) > \lambda\}} |f| \, d\mu.$

Thus by Theorem 2.2.3, when $f \in L_p$ $(p > 1)$, we obtain

$$\int_\Omega [R_n^*(f)]^p \, d\mu \leq \left(\frac{p}{p-1}\right)^p \int_\Omega |f|^p \, d\mu.$$

The inequality in 2.2.12 is then obtained by letting $n \to \infty$.

2.3 THE THEOREM OF DUNFORD AND SCHWARTZ

We have now more than we need to prove the following

ERGODIC THEOREM 2.3.1. *If T satisfies (1), (2), and (3), then for every $f \in L_p$ $(p \geq 1)$ as $n \to \infty$,*

2.3.1 $$R_n(f) = \frac{f + Tf + \cdots + T^n f}{n+1} \to Pf \quad \text{a.e.},$$

where Pf is defined according to Proposition 2.1.5.

PROOF. Let us first show 2.3.1 for $p > 1$. To this end for a given $f \in L_p$ define

$$g(f) = \limsup_{n\to\infty} R_n(f), \qquad h(f) = \liminf_{n\to\infty} R_n(f).$$

In view of 2.1.8 in Proposition 2.1.5 it follows that for any $\nu \geq 0$,

$$g\left(\frac{f + Tf + \cdots + T^\nu f}{\nu + 1} - Pf\right) = g(f) - Pf,$$

$$h\left(\frac{f + Tf + \cdots + T^\nu f}{\nu + 1} - Pf\right) = h(f) - Pf.$$

Using 2.2.12 with f replaced by $(f + \cdots + T^\nu f/\nu + 1) - Pf$ we then obtain, since both g and h are majorized by R^*,

$$\int_\Omega |g(f) - Pf|^p \, d\mu \leq \int_\Omega \left[R^*\left(\frac{f + \cdots + T^\nu f}{\nu + 1} - Pf\right)\right]^p d\mu$$
$$\leq \left(\frac{p}{p-1}\right)^p \int_\Omega |R_\nu(f) - Pf|^p \, d\mu.$$

Similarly,

$$\int_\Omega |h(f) - Pf|^p \, d\mu \leq \left(\frac{p}{p-1}\right)^p \int_\Omega |R_\nu(f) - Pf|^p \, d\mu.$$

This inequality must hold for all ν; thus by 2.1.7 of Proposition 2.1.5 we get

$$g(f) = h(f) = Pf \quad \text{a.e.}$$

To obtain the result for $p = 1$, it suffices to use the techniques of Theorem 1.1.1. Indeed, for any $\epsilon > 0$ we can find $g \in L_2$ such that

$$\int_\Omega |f - g| \, d\mu \leq \epsilon^2.$$

Then by writing $R_n(f) - Pf$ in the form

$$\frac{(f - g) + \cdots + T^n(f - g)}{n + 1} + P(g - f) + \frac{g + Tg + \cdots + T^n g}{n + 1} - Pg$$

and setting

$$\Omega(f) = \limsup_{n\to\infty} |R_n(f) - Pf|,$$

we obtain

$$\Omega(f) \leq R^*(f - g) + P|f - g|.$$

Therefore we get, by 2.2.8 and Proposition 2.1.5,

$$\mu\{\Omega(f) > \epsilon\} \leq \mu\left\{R^*(f - g) > \frac{\epsilon}{2}\right\} + \mu\left\{P|f - g| > \frac{\epsilon}{2}\right\}$$

$$\leq \frac{2}{\epsilon}\int_\Omega |f - g|\, d\mu + \frac{2}{\epsilon}\int_\Omega P|f - g|\, d\mu \leq 4\epsilon.$$

In other words,

$$\Omega(f) = \limsup_{n\to\infty} |R_n(f) - Pf| = 0 \quad \text{a.e.}$$

This establishes the theorem.

Remarks. Dunford and Schwartz have also shown that Theorem 2.3.1 remains valid even if we do not assume that T satisfies (1). We have developed enough tools here to be able to carry out the proof of convergence even in this case. There are two courses of action that may be followed. We could reprove Propositions 2.1.4 and 2.1.5 and Theorem 2.2.2 directly only under assumptions (2) and (3). This makes their proof slightly more cumbersome. The other course of action is to introduce, as Dunford and Schwartz do, another operator $\hat{T}$, by setting

$$\hat{T}f = \sup_{|g| \leq f} Tg \qquad \forall \quad f \geq 0.$$

This operator is easily shown to be linear, positive, and to satisfy (3) whenever T does. It is somewhat less elementary but quite straightforward to show that $\hat{T}$ satisfies also condition (2) (see [11]).

Since we trivially have

$$|Tf| \leq \hat{T}|f| \qquad \forall \quad f \in L_p \quad (p \geq 1)$$

from Theorem 2.2.2 and its Corollary 2.2.1 we immediately deduce

THEOREM 2.3.2. *If T satisfies* (2) *and* (3), *then*

$$2.3.2 \quad \int_\Omega [R^*(f)]^p\, d\mu \leq \left(\frac{p}{p-1}\right)^p \int_\Omega |f|^p\, d\mu \qquad \forall \quad f \in L_p \quad (p > 1)$$

and

$$\mu\{R^*f > \lambda\} \leq \frac{1}{\lambda}\int_\Omega |f|\, d\mu \qquad \forall \quad f \in L_p.$$

If we recall, the mean convergence result of Theorem 2.1.1 was established without any assumption of positivity for T. We can thus again define the operator P, and it automatically follows that P satisfies the conditions

(2) $|f| \leq C \Rightarrow |Pf| \leq C$ a.e.

(3) $\int_\Omega |Pf|\, d\mu \leq \int_\Omega |f|\, d\mu \qquad \forall \ f \in L_1 \cap L_\infty.$

In fact, we do have

$$\int_\Omega |Pf|^p\, d\mu \leq \int_\Omega |f|^p\, d\mu \qquad \forall \ p > 1 \ \text{ and } \ f \in L_1 \cap L_\infty;$$

thus the result must hold for $p = 1$. This shows that also in this case the definition of P can be extended to all $f \in L_1$. This given, the proof of the Ergodic Theorem 2.3.1 can be used word by word to show convergence without the assumption that T should be positive.

2.4 THE THEOREM OF CHACÓN AND ORNSTEIN

This section will be dedicated to the presentation of the theorem of Chacón and Ornstein. We shall thus be concerned with the almost everywhere convergence behavior of the ratios

$$R_n(f, g) = \frac{f + Tf + \cdots + T^n f}{g + Tg + \cdots + T^n g},$$

where $f, g \in L_1$, $g \geq 0$, and T is a linear operator of L_1 into L_1 which is only assumed to satisfy the two conditions

2.4.1 $$f \geq 0 \Rightarrow Tf \geq 0,$$

2.4.2 $$\int_\Omega |Tf|\, d\mu \leq \int_\Omega |f|\, d\mu \qquad \forall \ f \in L_1.$$

The above-mentioned result is the following

THEOREM 2.4.1. *If T is an operator satisfying* 2.4.1 *and* 2.4.2, *then for given $f, g \in L_1$, $g \geq 0$, the ratios*

$$R_n(f, g) = \frac{f + Tf + \cdots + T^n f}{g + Tg + \cdots + T^n g}$$

are almost everywhere convergent in the set when the denominators eventually become positive.

The existence of the limit, remarkable as it is in view of the weakness of the hypotheses under which it holds, is not by itself very illuminating as to the behavior of these ratios. For this reason we shall also present here the work of Chacón on the identification of the limit.

Many different proofs of these results are now available. Largely these new proofs have been stimulated by the work of Brunel [5]. Brunel discovered that the convergence result could be obtained in a remarkably simple way by means of a maximal ergodic inequality which seemed to be of a new type. Unfortunately, Brunel's proof of this inequality is intricate and not very illuminating. Several attempts have been made, the most noteworthy of them being those of Akcoglu [1] and Meyer [33], to obtain Brunel's inequality by a more revealing path. The extent to which these attempts have been successful is mostly a subjective matter. To those who know well the work of Chacón and Ornstein [10] and Chacón [9], Akcoglu's paper may appear to tell what is really behind Brunel's inequality. To those who are familiar with modern potential theory the work of Meyer may be more revealing. However, to those who do not possess any extra information the shortest path to Brunel's inequality up to now could still be found in Brunel's paper.

Because of all the literature that has flourished on this subject few people seem to be familiar with the contents of the now classical paper of Hopf [18], which was indeed the starting point of this branch of ergodic theory. We shall show here that it is now possible to give a very lucid and reasonably short proof of all these results, including Brunel's inequality, by following the rather natural line of reasoning adopted by Hopf. Indeed, we shall see that the only additional basic tool needed to carry out Hopf's original program is the following theorem which appears in the work of Chacón and Ornstein:

THEOREM 2.4.2. *If T is an operator satisfying* 2.4.1 *and* 2.4.2, *then for given $f \in L_1$, $p \in L_1$, $p \geq 0$ we have*

2.4.3 $$\lim_{n\to\infty} \frac{T^n f}{p + Tp + \cdots + T^n p} = 0$$

a.e. in the set where the denominators eventually become positive.

We shall also see via the above theorem that Brunel's inequality is nothing other than Hopf's maximal ergodic inequality (Theorem 2.2.1) in a disguised form.

Since the proof of Theorem 2.4.2 (which we are borrowing from Hopf [19]) does not require any preparation, we shall give it immediately. Notice first that we need only establish the result for nonnegative f's. The idea of the proof is then to show that for any given $\epsilon > 0$, the inequality

$$\frac{T^n f}{p + Tp + \cdots + T^n p} > \epsilon$$

can only occur finitely often a.e. in the set where $p > 0$. Or, in other words, if we introduce the function

$$\chi_n = \begin{cases} 1 & \text{when } T^n f > \epsilon(p + Tp + \cdots + T^n p), \\ 0 & \text{otherwise,} \end{cases}$$

then the series

$$\chi_1 + \chi_2 + \cdots + \chi_n + \cdots$$

is a.e. convergent in the set where $p > 0$.

The point of departure is the trivial identity

$$\epsilon p + T^n f - \epsilon \sum_{\nu=0}^{n} T^\nu p = T\left[T^{n-1} f - \epsilon \sum_{\nu=0}^{n-1} T^\nu p\right].$$

In view of 2.4.1 it follows then that

$$\epsilon p + T^n f - \epsilon \sum_{\nu=0}^{n} T^\nu p \leq T\left[T^{n-1} - \epsilon \sum_{\nu=0}^{n-1} T^\nu p\right]^+.$$

However, since the right-hand side of this inequality is always nonnegative, we must also have

$$\chi_n \epsilon p + \left[T^n f - \epsilon \sum_{\nu=0}^{n} T^\nu p\right]^+ \leq T\left[T^{n-1} f - \epsilon \sum_{\nu=0}^{n-1} T^\nu p\right]^+.$$

Integrating over Ω and using 2.4.2,

$$\epsilon \int_\Omega \chi_n p + \int_\Omega \left[T^n f - \epsilon \sum_{\nu=0}^{n} T^\nu p\right]^+ \leq \int_\Omega \left[T^{n-1} f - \epsilon \sum_{\nu=0}^{n-1} T^\nu p\right]^+.$$

Summing these inequalities for $n = 1, 2, \ldots, N$ we finally get

$$\epsilon \int_\Omega (\chi_1 + \chi_2 + \cdots + \chi_N)p \leq \int_\Omega [f - \epsilon p]^+ .$$

And this gives exactly what we need. By replacing f with Tf and p with Tp, we also get that for any $\epsilon > 0$ also the inequality

$$\frac{T^n f}{Tp + T^2 p + \cdots + T^n p} > \epsilon$$

can only occur finitely often a.e. in the set where $Tp > 0$. So the result is established completely by repeating this process with $T^2 p$, $T^3 p, \ldots$.

Remarks. The importance of the above theorem lies in the fact that it already assures the a.e. convergence of the ratios

$$R_n(f, p) = \frac{f + Tf + \cdots + T^n f}{p + Tp + \cdots + T^n p}$$

in the case when

$$f = g - Tg$$

for some $g \in L_1$. Indeed we then have

$$R_n(f, p) = \frac{g - T^{n+1} g}{p + Tp + \cdots + T^n p}.$$

So in the set where $p + Tp + \cdots + T^n p \to \infty$ we must have

$$R_n(f, p) \to 0 \quad \text{a.e.},$$

and in the set where $p + Tp + \cdots + T^n p + \cdots < \infty$ we get

$$R_n(f, p) \to \frac{g}{p + Tp + \cdots + T^n p + \cdots}.$$

It seems thus intuitive that by manipulations such as those carried out in the proof of Theorem 2.4.2 we might be able to show also that a.e. the ratios $R_n(f, p)$ oscillate only finitely many times over any given interval (α, β). This was indeed carried out very recently by Bishop [3], [4], who was able to establish an "upcrossing inequality" for these ratios. At this moment Bishop's approach does not seem to give the identification of the limit; its merit, however, lies in the fact that it yields a constructive approach to the

Chacón–Ornstein theorem and gives the shortest (if not the simplest) path to convergence. We have used the present method of proof because we personally feel that it contains more information on the reasons such results are true.

2.5 SOME BASIC PROPERTIES OF POSITIVE OPERATORS

In this section we shall present some basic properties of positive operators which will be crucial in the proof of the Chacón–Ornstein theorem.

To this end it is convenient to introduce the linear operator S of L_∞ into L_∞ characterized by the requirement that

$$\int_\Omega hTf = \int_\Omega fSh \qquad \forall \quad f \in L_1, h \in L_\infty .$$

It is easily verified that S has the following two properties, dual to 2.4.1 and 2.4.2:

2.5.1 $$h \geq 0 \Rightarrow Sh \geq 0,$$

2.5.2 $$|h| \leq 1 \Rightarrow |Sh| \leq 1 \quad \text{a.e.}$$

We also have the following proposition, dual to Proposition 2.1.2.

PROPOSITION 2.5.1. *If a sequence $h_n \in L_\infty$ converges a.e. and boundedly to h, then as $n \to \infty$,*

$$Sh_n \to Sh \quad \text{a.e.}$$

PROOF. Let $k_n = \sup_{m \geq n} |h_m - h|$. From the hypotheses it follows that

(a) $0 \leq k_n \leq C$ for some constant C;

(b) $k_n \downarrow 0$ a.e.

In view of 2.5.1, $Sk_n \downarrow \inf_{m \geq 1} Sk_m$. So we need only show that the latter function is a.e. zero. To this end we observe that for any $f \geq 0, f \in L_1$, we have

$$\int_\Omega [\inf_{m \geq 1} Sk_m] f \leq \int_\Omega [Sk_n] f = \int_\Omega k_n Tf, \qquad \forall \quad n \geq 1.$$

However, by dominated convergence the right-hand side of this inequality tends to zero as $n \to \infty$. So the result is established.

In analogy to what is done in the classical case when T comes from a measure-preserving transformation, a measurable set E will be called invariant if for its indicator χ_E we have

$$S\chi_E = \chi_E \quad \text{a.e.}$$

Similarly, a function $h \in L_\infty$ will be called invariant if

$$Sh = h \quad \text{a.e.}$$

From Proposition 2.5.1 we immediately deduce

PROPOSITION 2.5.2. *A boundedly convergent sequence of invariant function converges to an invariant function. In particular, a monotone sequence of invariant sets converges to an invariant set.*

Before we study further the properties of invariant sets and functions we need to establish a few important facts. We recall that under the hypotheses 2.4.1 and 2.4.2 the maximal ergodic inequality (Theorem 2.2.1) holds. Thus for any $\lambda > 0$ and any $f, p \in L_1$ we have

2.5.3 $$\int_{E(f-\lambda p)} (f - \lambda p) \geq 0,$$

where

$$E(f - \lambda p) = \{\sup_{n \geq 0} [(f + \cdots + T^n f) - \lambda(p + Tp + \cdots + T^n p)] > 0\}.$$

If we set for any measurable set E and a given $p > 0$,

$$\mu_p(E) = \int_E p \, d\mu,$$

then for the function

$$R^*(f, p) = \sup_{n \geq 0} |R_n(f, p)|,$$

we have the following basic

THEOREM 2.5.1. *If $f, p \in L_1$ and $p \geq 0$, then for any $\lambda > 0$ we have*

2.5.4 $$\mu_p\{R^*(f, p) > \lambda\} \leq \frac{1}{\lambda} \int_\Omega |f| \, d\mu.$$

This is obtained from 2.5.3 by observing that if $R^*(f, p) > \lambda$, then for some n we must have

$$|f| + \cdots + T^n|f| > \lambda(p + Tp + \cdots + T^n p).$$

We thus deduce that on the set where $p > 0$ we have

$$\sup_{n\geq 0}\left|\frac{f + Tf + \cdots + T^n f}{p + Tp + \cdots + T^n p}\right| < \infty \quad \text{a.e.}$$

This fact has very important consequences. Indeed, let us pick a fixed $\Phi \in L_1$, $\Phi > 0$, and define

$$\Omega_\infty = \{\Phi + T\Phi + \cdots + T^n\Phi \to \infty\},$$

$$\Omega_1 = \{\Phi + T\Phi + \cdots + T^n\Phi + \cdots < \infty\}.$$

It is clear that Ω_∞ and Ω_1 depend on the choice of Φ only up to a set of measure zero. For if Φ_1 is another such function we must have a.e. in Ω,

$$\sup_{n\geq 0}\frac{\Phi + T\Phi + \cdots + T^n\Phi}{\Phi_1 + T\Phi_1 + \cdots + T^n\Phi_1} < \infty,$$

$$\sup_{n\geq 0}\frac{\Phi_1 + T\Phi_1 + \cdots + T^n\Phi_1}{\Phi + T\Phi + \cdots + T^n\Phi} < \infty.$$

Also, since any function $f \in L_1$ can be written as the difference of two functions $\Phi_1, \Phi_2 \in L_1$ both > 0 a.e., we deduce that the ratios $R_n(f, g)$ for $f \in L_1$, $g \geq 0$ are a.e. convergent in Ω_1 in the set where the denominators eventually become positive. The limit there is just the ratio of two absolutely convergent series. The only real problem is thus convergence in Ω_∞.

The interesting fact is that the presence of Ω_1 makes convergence questions in Ω_∞ more difficult to study. For this reason we shall start our work under the assumption that

2.5.5 $$\mu(\Omega_1) = 0.$$

It will be seen that in the presence of this assumption the operator S and the invariant sets have remarkable properties. The first one is the following:

PROPOSITION 2.5.3. *A function $h \in L_\infty$ for which the difference $h - Sh$ has a.e. the same sign is necessarily invariant.*

PROOF. We can clearly assume $h \geq Sh$ a.e. We then have

$$\int_\Omega (h - Sh)[\Phi + T\Phi + \cdots + T^n\Phi]$$

$$= \int_\Omega h(1 - T)[\Phi + T\Phi + \cdots + T^n\Phi] = \int_\Omega h(\Phi - T^{n+1}\Phi).$$

And so, if $|h| \leq C$ a.e.,

$$\int_{\Omega} (h - Sh)[\Phi + T\Phi + \cdots + T^n\Phi] \leq C \int_{\Omega} [\Phi + T^{n+1}\Phi].$$

Since the right-hand side remains bounded as $n \to \infty$ and by assumption $\Phi + T\Phi + \cdots + T^n\Phi \to \infty$ a.e., we must have

$$h = Sh \quad \text{a.e.}$$

From this proposition follows the very important

PROPOSITION 2.5.4. *The class $\mathscr{I}$ of invariant sets is a Borel field.*

PROOF. Let h_1 and h_2 be invariant functions. Then we have

$$S(h_1 \vee h_2) \geq Sh_1 \vee Sh_2 = h_1 \vee h_2.\dagger$$

So $h_1 \vee h_2$ is invariant. Similarly, $h_1 \wedge h_2$ is invariant. It follows thus that the union and the intersection of two invariant sets are invariant. From property 2.5.2 of S it follows that $S1 \leq 1$ and thus we must also have $S1 = 1$ a.e.; consequently, the whole space is invariant. Therefore, also, the complement of an invariant set is invariant. Finally, countable unions and countable intersections of invariant sets must also be invariant, by Proposition 2.5.2. This completes the proof.

We also have the following remarkable

PROPOSITION 2.5.5. *A function $h \in L_\infty$ is invariant if and only if it is measurable with respect to the Borel field $\mathscr{I}$ of invariant sets.*

PROOF. If h is measurable with respect to $\mathscr{I}$, then h is the a.e. limit of a boundedly convergent sequence of simple invariant functions and therefore, by Proposition 2.5.2, it is also invariant.

To prove the converse, we need only show that if h is invariant, then for any $\alpha > 0$ the set

$$\{h > \alpha\} = \{h - \alpha > 0\}$$

is invariant. In other words, we are to show that the function

$$\chi = \begin{cases} 1 & \text{when } h > \alpha, \\ 0 & \text{otherwise,} \end{cases}$$

is invariant. To this end observe that the sequence of functions

$$\chi_n = n \min\left[(h - \alpha)^+, \frac{1}{n}\right]$$

† It is convenient to use the notation $a \vee b$ and $a \wedge b$ for max and min of a, b.

converges boundedly to χ. However, it is easy to see that each of the operations used in the definition of χ_n preserves invariance. Thus the assertion follows from Proposition 2.5.2.

We can finally conclude this section with the beautiful and illuminating result of Hopf.

PROPOSITION 2.5.6. *If h is invariant, then for any $f \in L_1$,*

2.5.6 $$Thf = hTf \quad \text{a.e.}$$

PROOF. Using Propositions 2.1.2 and 2.5.5 we can easily show we need only check the validity of 2.5.6 when h is the indicator of an invariant set. Then let $h = \chi_F$ with F invariant. Let ${}^cF$ denote the complement of F and let $f \geq 0$ be in L_1. We then trivially have

2.5.7 $$Tf = T\chi_F f + T\chi_{{}^cF} f.$$

On the other hand,

$$\int_\Omega \chi_{{}^cF} T\chi_F f = \int_\Omega S\gamma \quad \chi_F f = \int_\Omega \chi_{{}^cF}\chi_F f = 0.$$

This implies that

$$T\chi_F f = 0 \quad \text{a.e.} \quad \text{in } {}^cF;$$

similarly,

$$T\chi_{{}^cF} f = 0 \quad \text{a.e.} \quad \text{in } F.$$

Combining with 2.5.7 we get

$$T\chi_F f = \chi_F Tf, \qquad T\chi_{{}^cF} f = \chi_{{}^cF} Tf;$$

i.e., 2.5.6 must hold for χ_F as well as $\chi_{{}^cF}$.

Superficially, the time spent gathering the information expressed by the above propositions may seem out of proportion. However, we shall see that considerable insight has been gained, and we are now in a position to establish the results we are after with the greatest of ease. It should soon be clear that the effort put forth in this section is more than worthwhile.

2.6 CONVERGENCE WHEN $\Phi + T\Phi + \cdots + T^n\Phi \to \infty$ A.E.

Throughout this section we shall work under the assumption that $\mu(\Omega_1) = 0$. We shall later see how this restriction can be removed. One of the basic consequences of Theorem 2.4.2 and Proposition

2.5.6 is that the ratios $R_n(f, \Phi)$ do indeed converge when f can be written in the form

2.6.1 $$f = h\Phi + g - Tg,$$

where Φ and g are in L_1, $\Phi > 0$, and h is an invariant function. In fact, then

$$R_n(f, g) = h + \frac{g - T^{n+1}g}{\Phi + \cdots + T^n\Phi}.$$

Thus, in view of the hypothesis that $\Phi + T\Phi + \cdots + T^n\Phi \to \infty$ a.e., we get

2.6.2 $$\lim_{n\to\infty} R_n(f, \Phi) = h \quad \text{a.e.}$$

However, the functions of type 2.6.1 are dense in L_1. We can easily verify this fact by showing that if for some essentially bounded function k we have

2.6.3 $$\int_\Omega kf\,d\mu = 0 \qquad \forall \quad f \text{ of type 2.6.1},$$

then $k = 0$ a.e. Indeed, if

$$\int_\Omega k(g - Tg)\,d\mu = 0 \qquad \forall \quad g \in L_1,$$

the relation

$$\int_\Omega k(g - Tg)\,d\mu = \int_\Omega (k - Sk)g\,d\mu$$

gives

$$k = Sk \quad \text{a.e.}$$

This means we can take $h = k$ in 2.6.1. But then from 2.6.3 we get

$$\int_\Omega k^2\Phi\,d\mu = 0.$$

This establishes our assertion.

The estimate

2.6.4 $$\mu_\Phi\{R^*(f, \Phi) > \lambda\} \leq \frac{1}{\lambda}\int_\Omega |f|\,d\mu$$

can now be used (by Theorem 1.1.1) to deduce that the ratios $R_n(f, \Phi)$ converge a.e. for all $f \in L_1$. We shall, however, proceed in a slightly different fashion in order to obtain some information about the limit function.

Let f be of the form 2.6.1, and define

$$\chi = \begin{cases} 1 & \text{if } h \geq 0, \\ -1 & \text{if } h < 0. \end{cases}$$

By Proposition 2.5.5 χ is also invariant, and thus

$$\int_\Omega \chi(g - Tg)\, d\mu = 0.$$

Therefore,

2.6.5 $$\int_\Omega |h|\Phi\, d\mu = \int_\Omega \chi f\, d\mu \leq \int_\Omega |f|\, d\mu.$$

This inequality has some useful consequences. First, we deduce that for any given $f \in L_1$ there can be at most one h (up to equivalence) for which 2.6.1 can hold for some g. (This also follows from 2.6.2.) Therefore, the mapping $f \to h\Phi$ is well defined on the linear manifold of functions of type 2.6.1, and of course it is linear and homogeneous; in addition, the inequality 2.6.5 shows that it is bounded in the L_1 norm. We can thus conclude that this mapping has a unique extension to a bounded linear operator of L_1 into itself. If we denote this extension by P_Φ, 2.6.5 will then give

2.6.6 $$\int_\Omega |P_\Phi f|\, d\mu \leq \int_\Omega |f|\, d\mu \qquad \forall \; f \in L_1.$$

Let now $f, f_\epsilon \in L_1$ with

$$\|f - f_\epsilon\|_1 < \epsilon$$

and assume that f_ϵ is of the form 2.6.1. Then trivially

$$\left| R_n(f, \Phi) - \frac{P_\Phi f}{\Phi} \right| \leq \left| R_n(f - f_\epsilon, \Phi) \right| + \left| R_n(f_\epsilon, \Phi) - \frac{P_\Phi f_\epsilon}{\Phi} \right| + \left| \frac{P_\Phi(f_\epsilon - f)}{\Phi} \right|;$$

thus

$$2.6.7\quad \limsup_{n\to\infty}\left|R_n(f,\Phi)-\frac{P_\Phi f}{\Phi}\right|\le R^*(f-f_\epsilon,\Phi)+\left|\frac{P_\Phi(f_\epsilon-f)}{\Phi}\right|.$$

From 2.6.4 we deuce that

$$\mu_\Phi\{R^*(f-f_\epsilon,\Phi)>\sqrt{\epsilon}\}\le\frac{1}{\sqrt{\epsilon}}\epsilon=\sqrt{\epsilon}$$

and, from 2.6.6,

$$\mu_\Phi\left\{\left|\frac{P_\Phi(f_\epsilon-f)}{\Phi}\right|>\sqrt{\epsilon}\right\}\le\sqrt{\epsilon}.$$

Combining these two inequalities with 2.6.7, we deuce that

$$\mu_\Phi\left\{\limsup_{n\to\infty}\left|R_n(f,\Phi)-\frac{P_\Phi f}{\Phi}\right|>2\sqrt{\epsilon}\right\}\le 2\sqrt{\epsilon}.$$

Since ϵ is arbitrary, we obtain

$$\lim_{n\to\infty}R_n(f,\Phi)=\frac{P_\Phi f}{\Phi}\qquad\forall\quad f\in L_1.$$

Finally, note that for any invariant set Λ we have

$$\int_\Lambda(g-Tg)\,d\mu=\int_\Omega(\chi_\Lambda-S\chi_\Lambda)g\,d\mu=0\qquad\forall\quad g\in L_1.$$

Consequently, we must have

$$\int_\Lambda f\,d\mu=\int_\Lambda P_\Phi f\,d\mu$$

for all f of the form 2.6.1 and thus also for all $f\in L_1$.

We can recapitulate the results we have obtained by the following.

THEOREM 2.6.1. *When $\mu(\Omega_1)=0$ and for a fixed $\Phi>0$ in L_1 the ratios $R_n(f,\Phi)$ converge a.e. $\forall\ f\in L_1$. Further, if we denote this limit function by $h(f,\Phi)$, we have*

(a) *$h(f,\Phi)$ is measurable with respect to the field $\mathcal{I}$ of invariant sets.*

(b) *The mapping $P_\Phi f=h(f,\Phi)\Phi$ is a positive linear operator which is a contraction of L_1 into itself.*

(c) *For all* $\Lambda \in \mathscr{I}$ *and for all* $f \in L_1$ *we have*

2.6.8 $$\int_\Lambda h(f, \Phi)\Phi \, d\mu = \int_\Lambda f \, d\mu.$$

It is not difficult to deduce from this theorem the convergence result for general ratios $R_n(f, g)$ with $f, g \in L_1$ and g only assumed ≥ 0. We leave this to the reader. It is more interesting to study at this point Brunel's maximal inequality, since we are now in a position to understand its real meaning.

2.7 BRUNEL'S INEQUALITY

In this section, unless otherwise stated, *we shall not* assume that $\mu(\Omega_1) = 0$. Before presenting Brunel's result it is convenient to introduce what we shall call the "Brunel function" of a given measurable set E. To this end, we introduce the sequence $\Psi_E^{(m)}$ of bounded functions by the inductive relations

2.7.1 $$\Psi_E^{(m)} = \chi_E \vee S\Psi_E^{(m-1)}, \qquad \Psi_E^{(0)} = \chi_E,$$

where, as we have done before, χ_E is the indicator of the set E, S is the operator adjoint of T, and the symbol $\vee$ denotes the operation of taking the maximum. We observe that since S is a positive contraction in L_∞, we shall have, by induction

2.7.2 $$0 \leq \Psi_E^{(m)} \leq 1 \qquad \forall \quad m.$$

Before proceeding any further it is both convenient and illuminating to rewrite the defining relations 2.7.1. Note that in view of 2.7.2 we must have

$$\Psi_E^{(m)} = \begin{cases} \chi_E \text{ in } E \\ S\Psi_E^{(m-1)} \text{ in } {}^cE \end{cases} = \chi_E + \chi_{^cE} S\Psi_E^{(m-1)}.$$

Thus, if we introduce the operator V_E by the relation

$$V_E h = \chi_{^cE} Sh \qquad \forall \quad h \in L_\infty,$$

we can write 2.7.1 in the form

2.7.3 $$\Psi_E^{(m)} = \chi_E + V_E \Psi_E^{(m-1)}$$

and so, by induction, we get

2.7.4 $$\Psi_E^{(m)} = \chi_E + V_E \chi_E + \cdots + V_E^m \chi_E.$$

This relation shows in particular that the sequence $\Psi_E^{(m)}$ is increasing. By 2.7.2, it must have a limit. This limit is what we shall call the Brunel function of the set E. We shall denote it by Ψ_E. Let us study some of its basic properties. First, by the very definition we must have

2.7.5 $$\chi_E \leq \Psi_E \leq 1.$$

Second, by virtue of Proposition 2.5.1, passing to the limit in relation 2.7.3 we obtain

2.7.6 $$\Psi_E = \chi_E + V_E \Psi_E = \chi_E \vee S\Psi_E.$$

Finally, by repetitive use of the above relation we obtain

$$\Psi_E = \chi_E + V_E \chi_E + \cdots + V_E^m \chi_E + V_E^{m+1} \Psi_E = \Psi_E^{(m)} + V_E^{m+1} \Psi_E.$$

So we must conclude that

2.7.7 $$\lim_{n \to \infty} V_E^{m+1} \Psi_E = 0 \quad \text{a.e.}$$

As we shall later see, this fact is of fundamental importance. We can now state Brunel's maximal ergodic inequality.

THEOREM 2.7.1 (*Akcoglu's form*). *Let $f \in L_1$ and suppose that we have*

2.7.8 $$f + Tf + \cdots + T^n f > 0 \qquad \text{infinitely often in } E;$$

i.e., this inequality occurs at each point of a set E for infinitely many n, then

2.7.9 $$\int_\Omega \Psi_E f \, d\mu \geq 0.$$

Originally, Brunel proved the above result with 2.7.8 replaced by the stronger condition that for any n

$$\sup_{m \geq 0} (T^n f + \cdots + T^{n+m} f) > 0 \quad \text{in } E.$$

The latter hypothesis is rather cumbersome and tends to hide the real origin of Theorem 2.7.1. It was Akcoglu who discovered that the theorem is valid under the very simple condition 2.7.8.

At this moment the reader, unfamiliar with this subject, may rightly wonder how anyone could be led even to conjecture such a result as Theorem 2.7.1. Since none of the proofs that are presently available in the literature seem to throw any light on this matter, it might be worthwhile, before proceeding with the proof, to use some of the information we have already at hand in order to obtain a little more insight.

There has been for years a very tempting approach to the proof of convergence which is based upon the Hopf maximal ergodic inequality (Theorem 2.2.1). Indeed, we have seen that the ratios $R_n(f, \Phi)$ do converge in Ω_1; however, even in Ω_∞ they can at worst oscillate finitely. If there is a divergence set of positive measure, then there must be at least two reals $\alpha < \beta$ such that in some set E of positive measure we simultaneously have

2.7.10
$$\limsup_{n\to\infty} R_n(f, \Phi) > \beta,$$
$$\liminf_{n\to\infty} R_n(f, \Phi) < \alpha.$$

This in turn implies that

2.7.11
$$(f - \beta\Phi) + \cdots + T^n(f - \beta\Phi) > 0 \qquad \text{infinitely often in } E,$$
$$(\alpha\Phi - f) + \cdots + T^n(\alpha\Phi - f) > 0 \qquad \text{infinitely often in } E.$$

In particular, E must be contained in both Hopf's sets $E(f - \beta\Phi)$, $E(\alpha\Phi - f)$. Now, Hopf's maximal ergodic inequality gives

$$\int_{E(f-\beta\Phi)} (f - \beta\Phi)\, d\mu \geq 0, \qquad \int_{E(\alpha\Phi - f)} (\alpha\Phi - f)\, d\mu \geq 0.$$

If perchance both sets $E(f - \beta\Phi)$, $E(\alpha\Phi - f)$ are equal to the same set, say F, then upon adding these two inequalities we would get

$$(\alpha - \beta)\int_F \Phi\, d\mu \geq 0.$$

But this is absurd unless $\int_F \Phi\, d\mu = 0$. However, since E is supposed to have positive measure and $\Phi > 0$, we must have

$$\int_F \Phi\, d\mu \geq \int_E \Phi\, d\mu > 0.$$

The argument would indeed give a rather simple proof of convergence. Unfortunately, in general we cannot guarantee that these two sets be the same, and so this method seems at first sight to be doomed to failure. It turns out that the idea at least can be salvaged by means of two fundamental observations.

First, we notice that in the above argument we fail to use the fact that the inequalities in 2.7.11 are satisfied not only for at least one n but infinitely often.

Second, Hopf's maximal ergodic theorem is valid also in the following (only apparently) more general form.

THEOREM 2.7.2. *If T is a positive bounded linear operator of L_1 into L_1 and Ψ is a bounded positive function satisfying the inequality*

2.7.12 $$S\Psi \leq \Psi,$$

where S is the adjoint of T, then for any $f \in L_1$ we have

$$\int_{E(f)} f\Psi \, d\mu \geq 0,$$

where

$$E(f) = \{\sup_{n \geq 0} (f + Tf + \cdots + T^n f) > 0\}.$$

PROOF. This is merely a restatement of Theorem 2.2.1. In fact, it can be obtained directly from that theorem upon replacing μ by the measure

$$\mu_\Psi(E) = \int_E \Psi \, d\mu.$$

For, 2.7.12 implies that

$$\int_\Omega |Tf|\Psi \, d\mu \leq \int_\Omega |f|\Psi \, d\mu \qquad \forall \quad f \in L_1,$$

and thus under these hypotheses T is a contraction in $L_1(\Omega, \mathscr{F}, \mu_\Psi)$.

Bearing in mind these facts, we might hope that although the sets $E(f - \beta\Phi)$, $E(\alpha\Phi - f)$ could be different, in the presence of the hypotheses 2.7.11 they may still turn out to agree on the support of some nonnegative function Ψ satisfying 2.7.12.

Indeed, this is essentially what happens with the Brunel function Ψ_E. Remarkably enough, in the case that $\mu(\Omega_1) = 0$, it can be shown that if the relation

$$f + Tf + \cdots + T^n f > 0$$

holds infinitely often in a set E, then it must hold infinitely often also in the support of Ψ_E.

This is all to the good; however, it does not explain yet how anyone could be led to choose Ψ_E among all the functions satisfying 2.7.12. To find the path that will lead us to the exact form of Ψ_E we must study what happens in the case that $\mu(\Omega_1) = 0$.

It is easy to see, using the full power of Theorem 2.6.1, that both sets

$$\{\limsup_{n\to\infty} R_n(f, \Phi) \geq \beta\}, \qquad \{\liminf_{n\to\infty} R_n(f, \Phi) \leq \alpha\}$$

are invariant; thus their intersection F is also invariant. This shows that if the inequalities in 2.7.11 occur in a set E, then there is an invariant set F containing E on which the same inequalities do hold as well. Thus a proof along the lines indicated above could be obtained by taking $\Psi = \chi_F$ in Theorem 2.7.2.

We are thus led, in order to obtain a proof of convergence that is independent of Theorem 2.6.1, to show that if an inequality such as that in 2.7.8 holds infinitely often in a set E, then it must keep on holding at least in the smallest possible invariant set F containing E.

Let us see how small can this invariant set be. We clearly must have

$$\chi_F \geq \chi_E, \qquad \chi_F = S\chi_F \geq S\chi_E$$

and so also

$$\chi_F \geq \chi_E \vee S\chi_E.$$

Therefore again

$$\chi_F \geq \chi_E \vee S(\chi_E \vee S\chi_E).$$

We are thus led to the sequence introduced in 2.7.1.

Before we go to our proof of Brunel's lemma, it is worthwhile pushing the above reasoning a bit further. Notice, we have shown that if an invariant set F contains E, then

$$\chi_F \geq \Psi_E^{(m)}$$

$\forall\, m \geq 0$. Consequently, we must have

$$\chi_F \geq \Psi_E.$$

But now we know that when $\mu(\Omega_1) = 0$, the set $F = \{\Psi_E = 1\}$ *is* invariant! Since $\Psi_E = 1$ on E, this set contains E. And we must conclude that

$$\Psi_E = \chi_{\{\Psi_E = 1\}}.$$

In other words, when $\mu(\Omega_1) = 0$, Ψ_E is the indicator of the smallest invariant set which contains E. And, therefore, in this case it is clear that if the inequality

$$f + Tf + \cdots + T^n f > 0$$

holds infinitely often in E, it must hold infinitely often in the support of Ψ_E. So it is evident here that Brunel's theorem is nothing but Hopf's maximal ergodic inequality in a disguised form.

The heuristic line of reasoning expounded above cannot be made into a proof without some tortuous modifications when $\mu(\Omega_1) \neq 0$. Thus, in order to reach the result by the shortest possible path, we shall follow here a slightly different argument.

PROOF OF THEOREM 2.7.1. First, we observe that there is no loss in proving the theorem under the hypothesis

2.7.13 $$f + Tf + \cdots + T^n f > \epsilon(\Phi + T\Phi + \cdots + T^n\Phi) \quad \text{infinitely often in } E.$$

For, if f satisfies 2.7.8, then $f + \epsilon\Phi$ satisfies 2.7.13, and once we have gotten $\int_\Omega (f + \epsilon\Phi)\Psi_E \, d\mu \geq 0 \ \forall \ \epsilon > 0$, 2.7.9 must necessarily follow.

From the definition of Ψ_E we get

$$\int_\Omega f\Psi_E \, d\mu = \lim \int_\Omega f\Psi_E^{(m)} \, d\mu.$$

Introducing the operator $U_E f = T\chi_{cE} f$ (the adjoint of V_E) we can write, in view of 2.7.4,

2.7.14 $$\int_\Omega f\Psi_E^{(m)} \, d\mu = \int_\Omega \chi_E(f + U_E f + \cdots + U_E^m f) \, d\mu.$$

We are thus led to consider the function

$$g_m = f + U_E f + \cdots + U_E^m f.$$

Of course, if as a consequence of 2.7.13 we could show that

$$E \subset \{\sup_{n \geq 0} (\chi_E g_m + \cdots + T^n \chi_E g_m) > 0\},$$

then we would be done. It turns out this is almost true.

In fact, it is easy to verify that

$$f = \chi_E g_m + U_E^{m+1} f + \chi_{c_E} g_m - T\chi_{c_E} g_m;$$

therefore,

$$R_n(f, \Phi) = R_n(\chi_E g_m + U_E^{m+1} f, \Phi) + \frac{\chi_{c_E} g_m - T^{n+1} \chi_{c_E} g_m}{\Phi + T\Phi + \cdots + T^n \Phi}.$$

Now, by Theorem 2.4.2 we get that in E

$$\lim_{n \to \infty} \frac{\chi_{c_E} g_m - T^{n+1} \chi_{c_E} g_m}{\Phi + T\Phi + \cdots + T^n \Phi} = 0 \quad \text{a.e.}$$

We must thus conclude that, except for a set of measure zero,

$$E \subset E_m = \{\sup_{n \geq 0} [(\chi_E g_m + U_E^{m+1} f) + \cdots + T^n(\chi_E g_m + U_E^{m+1} f)] > 0\}$$

Using Hopf's maximal ergodic theorem in the form of Theorem 2.7.2 we obtain

$$\int_{E_m} (\chi_E g_m + U_E^{m+1} f) \Psi_E \, d\mu \geq 0.$$

But this gives

$$\int_\Omega f \Psi_E^{(m)} \, d\mu = \int_E g_m \, d\mu \geq - \int_\Omega (U_E^{m+1} |f|) \Psi_E \, d\mu$$

$$= - \int_\Omega |f| V_E^{m+1} \Psi_E \, d\mu.$$

Passing to the limit as $m \to \infty$ and using 2.7.7, we get our desired inequality.

Remark. Now that Brunel's inequality has been established, we have finally in our possession a proof of the theorem of Chacón–Ornstein without any exceptions. Although this was not explicitly done, it is not difficult to fill in the remaining steps. In the next section we shall be concerned with the identification of the limit in the general case that $\mu(\Omega_1) \neq 0$; as a by-product we shall also encounter another way of establishing the convergence result.

2.8 CONVERGENCE AND IDENTIFICATION OF THE LIMIT IN THE GENERAL CASE

Once the convergence result has been obtained in the case $\mu(\Omega_1) = 0$, it is not difficult nowadays to obtain the convergence result in the general case. The first step in this direction is given by the following fact discovered by Hopf.

THEOREM 2.8.1. *If $f \in L_1$ and $f = 0$ in Ω_1, then $Tf = 0$ a.e. in Ω_1. Equivalently, the function χ_{Ω_1} satisfies the inequality*

2.8.1 $$S\chi_{\Omega_1} \leq \chi_{\Omega_1} \quad \text{a.e.}$$

PROOF. Let us verify that the two statements above are really equivalent. It is easy to see that the first statement is equivalent to

$$0 = \int_\Omega \chi_{\Omega_1} Tf \, d\mu = \int_\Omega f S\chi_{\Omega_1} \, d\mu \qquad \forall \; f \in L_1, f = 0 \text{ in } \Omega_1,$$

and the latter statement is equivalent to saying that

2.8.2 $$S\chi_{\Omega_1} = 0 \quad \text{a.e.} \quad \text{in } \Omega_\infty,$$

and this (since $S\chi_{\Omega_1} \leq 1$) is equivalent to 2.8.1.

Then let $E \subset \Omega_\infty$ be a measurable set of finite measure. Set, for a fixed $\lambda > 0$,

$$E_m = \{\Phi + T\Phi + \cdots + T^m\Phi > \lambda\} \cap E.$$

We then have

$$\lambda\chi_{E_m} \leq \Phi + T\Phi + \cdots + T^m\Phi$$

and consequently, by the positivity of T,

2.8.3 $$\lambda T\chi_{E_m} \leq T\Phi + T^2\Phi + \cdots + T^{m+1}\Phi.$$

Now, the function

$$G = \Phi + T\Phi + \cdots + T^n\Phi + \cdots$$

is well defined in Ω_1, and thus we must have (by 2.8.3)

$$\lambda T\chi_{E_m} \leq G.$$

Letting $m \to \infty$ we get

$$\lambda T\chi_E \le G,$$

and since λ is arbitrary, we deduce that

$$T\chi_E = 0 \text{ in } \Omega_1 .$$

Integrating this relation over Ω_1, we get

$$0 = \int_\Omega \chi_{\Omega_1} T\chi_E \, d\mu = \int_\Omega \chi_E S\chi_{\Omega_1} \, d\mu.$$

Since E is an arbitrary set of finite measure contained in Ω_∞, 2.8.2 must necessarily hold.

Let us study the implications of this result. The class of functions $f \in L_1(\Omega, \mathscr{F}, \mu)$ which vanish in Ω_1 can obviously be identified with $L_1(\Omega_\infty, \mathscr{F}, \mu)$. Theorem 2.8.1 says that T maps $L_1(\Omega_\infty, \mathscr{F}, \mu)$ into itself. Now, note that for any function $\Phi_1 \in L_1(\Omega_\infty, \mathscr{F}, \mu)$ and > 0 in Ω_∞ we necessarily have

$$\Phi_1 + T\Phi_1 + \cdots + T^n\Phi_1 \to \infty \quad \text{a.e.} \quad \text{in } \Omega_\infty .$$

This is because (Theorem 2.5.1)

$$R^*(\Phi, \Phi_1) < \infty \text{ a.e.} \qquad \text{on the set where } \Phi_1 > 0.$$

Therefore, we can apply to T, qua operator on $L_1(\Omega_\infty, \mathscr{F}, \mu)$, the theory we have developed in 2.5 and 2.6. We can thus conclude that the ratios $R_n(f, g)$ are almost everywhere convergent in Ω_∞ whenever $f, g \in L_1$, $g > 0$ in Ω_∞, and $f, g = 0$ in Ω_1.

The only missing step now is that which will permit us to replace general ratios $R_n(f, g)$ by ratios involving functions f, g which vanish outside Ω_∞. We will have no difficulty in carrying out this step if we use some of the tools we have already at hand.

Note that the function $\Psi_E^{(m)}$ of the last section can be thought of as the result of applying the operator

2.8.4 $$K_E^{(m)} = (I + V_E + \cdots + V_E^m)\chi_E$$

to the function 1. In the same vein the function $\chi_E g_m$ is the result of applying to f the adjoint operator

2.8.5 $$H_E^{(m)} = \chi_E(I + U_E + \cdots + U_E^m).$$

For $f \geq 0$ and in L_1 we have

2.8.6 $$\int_\Omega H_E^{(m)} f \, d\mu \leq \int_\Omega f \Psi_E^{(m)} \, d\mu \leq \int_\Omega f \, d\mu.$$

Thus by monotone convergence we deduce that the limit

$$H_E f = \lim_{n \to \infty} H_E^{(m)} f$$

exists and is in L_1. By linearity this limit must exist for all $f \in L_1$. From 2.8.6 we deduce that the operator H_E which it defines has the basic properties

2.8.7
(a) $f \geq 0 \Rightarrow H_E f \geq 0$;

(b) $\int_\Omega |H_E f| \, d\mu \leq \int_\Omega |f| \, d\mu \quad \forall \; f \in L_1$.

The remarkable fact is that as far as the a.e. behavior in E of the ratios R_n is concerned, the functions f and $H_E f$ are completely interchangeable. More precisely:

THEOREM 2.8.2. *For any $f \in L_1$ we have*

2.8.8 $$\lim_{n \to \infty} [R_n(f, \Phi) - R_n(H_E f, \Phi)] = 0 \quad \text{a.e.} \quad \text{in } E.$$

This result was conjectured by Hopf in the case that $E = \Omega_\infty$ and was part of Hopf's original program for the convergence proof. It was proved somewhat later by Chacón [9] under a restrictive assumption on E, namely that

2.8.9 $$S\chi_{c_E} \leq \chi_{c_E}.$$

As we have seen, this is satisfied in the case that $E = \Omega_\infty$.

We thus see that at least the adjoint of the operator which gives Ψ_E had already been considered in the literature and for good reasons, before Brunel's paper. The additional implication we seem to get here by means of the Brunel function is that in order to establish 2.8.8 the assumption 2.8.9 can be omitted.

PROOF OF THEOREM 2.8.2. We start from the identity we had in the previous section, namely

$$f = \chi_E g_m + U_E^{m+1} f + \chi_{c_E} g_m - T\chi_{c_E} g_m.$$

By Theorem 2.4.2 we deduce then that in E

$$\limsup_{n \to \infty} |R_n(f, \Phi) - R_n(H_E^m f, \Phi)| \leq R^*(U_E^{m+1} f, \Phi),$$

and therefore we have

2.8.10 $$\limsup_{n\to\infty} |R_n(f, \Phi) - R_n(H_E f, \Phi)| \le R^*(U_E^{m+1} f, \Phi) + R^*(H_E f - H_E^{(m)} f, \Phi).$$

From Hopf's maximal ergodic theorem in the form 2.7.2 with $\Psi = \Psi_E$ we readily get

$$\mu_\Phi[\{R^*(U^{m+1} f, \Phi) > \epsilon\} \cap E] \le \int_{\{R^*(U_E^{m+1} f, \Phi) > \epsilon\}} \Phi \Psi_E \, d\mu \le \frac{1}{\epsilon} \int_\Omega (U_E^{m+1} |f|) \Psi_E \, d\mu.$$

At the same time we do have

$$\mu_\Phi\{R^*(H_E f - H_E^{(m)} f, \Phi) > \epsilon\} \le \frac{1}{\epsilon} \int_\Omega |H_E f - H_E^{(m)} f| \, d\mu.$$

Both right-hand sides of these two inequalities can be made arbitrarily small, say less than ϵ, by choosing m large enough; the first by 2.7.7 and the second by the definition of H_E. Combining this fact with 2.8.10 we get

$$\mu_\Phi\{\limsup_{n\to\infty} |R_n(f, \Phi) - R_n(H_E f, \Phi)| > 2\epsilon\} \cap E \le 2\epsilon.$$

Since ϵ is arbitrary, 2.8.8 must necessarily hold.

We have now all the tools we need to establish the final result. Let $\mathscr{I}$ be the class of measurable sets F which satisfy the condition

$$S\chi_F = \chi_F \quad \text{a.e.} \quad \text{in } \Omega_\infty.$$

The elements of $\mathscr{I}$ will play here the role that the invariant sets played in Section 2.6. It is also easy to show using the results of Section 2.5 that $\mathscr{I}$ is a Borel field. We can finally state.

THEOREM 2.8.3. *For a fixed $\Phi > 0$ in L_1 the ratios $R_n(f, \Phi)$ converge a.e. $\forall f \in L_1$. Further if we denote this limit by $h(f, \Phi)$, we have*

(a) *In Ω_1*

$$h(f, \Phi) = \frac{\lim\limits_{n\to\infty} \sum\limits_{\nu=0}^{n} T^\nu f}{\lim\limits_{n\to\infty} \sum\limits_{\nu=0}^{n} T^\nu \Phi}.$$

(b) *The behavior of* $h(f, \Phi)$ *in* Ω_∞ *is characterized by the fact that there* $h(f, \Phi) = \lim_{n\to\infty} R_n(H_E f, H_E \Phi)$, *and therefore we must have*

(a) The function $h(f, \Phi)$ is measurable with respect to $\mathscr{I}$.

(b) The mapping $P_\Phi f = h(f, \Phi)H_E\Phi$ is a positive linear operator that is a contraction of L_1.

(c) For all $\Lambda \in \mathscr{I}$ and for all $f \in L_1$ we have

$$\int_\Lambda h(f, \Phi)H_E\Phi \, d\mu = \int_\Lambda H_E f \, d\mu.$$

PROOF. We need only establish that

$$\lim_{n\to\infty} [R_n(f, \Phi) - R_n(H_E f, H_E\Phi)] = 0 \quad \text{a.e.} \quad \text{in } \Omega_\infty.$$

However, this follows easily from Theorem 2.8.2 and Theorem 2.5.1 by means of the trivial inequalities

$$|R_n(f, H_E\Phi) - R_n(H_E f, H_E\Phi)|$$
$$\leq |R_n(f, \Phi) - R_n(H_E f, \Phi)| R^*(\Phi, H_E\Phi),$$
$$|R_n(f, H_E\Phi) - R_n(f, \Phi)|$$
$$\leq |R_n(H_E\Phi, \Phi) - R_n(\Phi, \Phi)| R^*(f, H_E\Phi).$$

3

COMBINATORIAL INEQUALITIES AND CONVERGENCE ALMOST EVERYWHERE OF SOME ORTHOGONAL EXPANSIONS

Given a system of functions $\{\Phi_n(\omega)\}\,(n = 1, 2,\ldots)$ that is orthonormal in a measure space $(\Omega, \mathscr{F}, \mu)$, it is an elementary fact that the partial sums

$$S_n(x, f) = \sum_{\nu=1}^{n} a_\nu \Phi_\nu(x) \qquad \left(a_\nu = \int_\Omega f(x)\Phi_\nu(x)\, d\mu\right)$$

of the Fourier expansion of a function in $L_2(\Omega, \mathscr{F}, d\mu)$ converges in the L_2 sense, and toward the function f if the system is complete.

However, the sequence $S_n(x, f)$ does not necessarily converge in the almost everywhere sense unless the system $\{\Phi_n(x)\}$ satisfies some additional conditions. This fact, which was discovered many years ago by Menschov [30], is by no means obvious; indeed, Menshov's examples are quite elaborate. Keeping this in mind and in view of some of the latest results [13] and especially [8] in this field, there is reason to believe that for some large class of orthonormal systems the sequence $S_n(x, f)$ does converge almost everywhere for all $f \in L_2$.

In this connection there is also another phenomenon that has to be taken into account. If $\sigma = (\sigma_1, \sigma_2, \ldots, \sigma_n, \ldots)$ denotes a permutation of the integers $(1, 2,\ldots, n,\ldots)$, we might be inclined, from the L_2 viewpoint, to consider the systems $\{\Phi_n(x)\}$ and $\{\Phi_{\sigma_n}(x)\}$ as essentially identical. Yet the partial sums of the expansions

$$S_n(x, f) = \sum_{\nu=1}^{n} a_\nu \Phi_\nu(x) \qquad \text{and} \qquad S_n(x, \sigma, f) = \sum_{\nu=1}^{n} a_{\sigma_\nu} \Phi_{\sigma_\nu}(x)$$

of the same function f with respect to $\{\Phi_n(x)\}$ and $\{\Phi_{\sigma_n}(x)\}$ can have a quite different almost everywhere behavior.

In fact, it has been shown mainly by the Russian school that any complete orthonormal system $\{\Phi_n\}$ on $[0, 1]$ admits a rearrangement $\{\Phi_{\sigma_n}\}$ which is such that for some function $f \in L_2$ the partial sums $S_n(x, \sigma, f)$ diverge almost everywhere. In particular, we can take the Haar system, for which the partial sums are almost everywhere convergent for all $f \in L_2$ and spoil it by a suitable permutation. We shall not be concerned with this topic here. A rather exhaustive account of these results and a vast bibliography may be found in Uljanov's papers ([41] and [42]).

We shall proceed here in the opposite direction and present a new proof of the following result [13]. Namely, that given any system $\{\Phi_n\}$ and any function $f \in L_2$ there always is a rearrangement $\{\Phi_{\sigma_n}\}$ such that the partial sums $S_n(x, \sigma, f)$ of the Fourier series of f with respect to $\{\Phi_{\sigma_n}\}$ converge almost everywhere.

This leads us to a question that as far as we know is still open: whether or not, bad as a system may be, it is possible to find a permutation σ such that the $S_n(x, \sigma, f)$'s converge almost everywhere for all $f \in L_2$ $(\Omega, \mathscr{F}, d\mu)$.

If the answer to this question is affirmative, then it must be that for systems $\{\Phi_n\}$ which are of such a nature that they are essentially left unchanged by any permutation, the almost everywhere result must hold automatically. These are systems which are such that for any n and reals $\alpha_1, \alpha_2, \ldots, \alpha_n$ the equality

$$\mu\{\Phi_1 \leq \alpha_1, \Phi_2 \leq \alpha_2, \ldots, \Phi_n \leq \alpha_n\}$$
$$= \mu\{\Phi_{\sigma_1} \leq \alpha_1, \Phi_{\sigma_2} \leq \alpha_2, \ldots, \Phi_{\sigma_n} \leq \alpha_n\}$$

holds for every permutation $\sigma = (\sigma_1, \sigma_2, \ldots, \sigma_n)$ of $(1, 2, \ldots, n)$. We shall see here that this is indeed true, and in the process we shall obtain some very interesting combinatorial inequalities involving partial sums of real numbers.

However, before presenting the above material we shall need a review of some of the basic tools that have been developed in this subject. In particular we shall also present two interesting proofs of the Martingale theorem.

3.1 JENSEN-TYPE INEQUALITIES

In this section, to avoid technicalities, "a convex function" shall mean a function $\Phi(u)$ defined in $[-\infty, +\infty]$ which can be written in the form

3.1.1 $$\Phi(u) = a + bu + \int_0^u (u - \sigma)\varphi(\sigma)\, d\sigma,$$

where $\varphi(\sigma)$ is assumed to be nonnegative and integrable in any finite interval.†

As before, T will denote a linear operator of $L_1(\Omega, \mathscr{F}, d\mu)$ into itself which satisfies the conditions

(a) $f \geq 0 \Rightarrow Tf \geq 0$;

3.1.2 (b) $\int_\Omega |Tf|\, d\mu \leq \int_\Omega |f|\, d\mu \qquad \forall\ f \in L_1$;

(c) $|f| \leq C \Rightarrow |Tf| \leq C$.

We then start as we did in Section 2.1 with the inequality

3.1.3 $$(Tf - C)^+ \leq (f - C)^+,$$

which is valid, in view of (a) and (c), for all $f \geq 0$ and in L_1. Integrating 3.1.3 over Ω and using 3.1.2(c) we get as before

3.1.4 $$\int_\Omega (Tf - C)^+\, d\mu \leq \int_\Omega (f - C)^+\, d\mu.$$

We can now prove

PROPOSITION 3.1.1. *If $\Phi(u)$ is convex with $b \geq 0$ in* 3.1.1 *and T is an operator satisfying the conditions* 3.1.2, *then*

3.1.5 $$\int_\Omega \Phi(|Tf|)\, d\mu \leq \int_\Omega \Phi(|f|)\, d\mu.$$

Furthermore, even if $\Phi(u)$ decreases somewhere, this inequality remains valid at least for $f \geq 0$ when $\int_\Omega Tf\, d\mu = \int_\Omega f\, d\mu$.

PROOF. Clearly we need only show 3.1.5 when $a = b = 0$ in 3.1.1. This given, if we multiply 3.1.4 by $\varphi(C)$ and integrate from 0 to ∞ we obtain

$$\int_\Omega \Phi(Tf)\, d\mu \leq \int_\Omega \Phi(f)\, d\mu$$

for all $f \geq 0$. But then, if $\Phi(u)$ is nondecreasing, the inequality $\Phi(|Tf|) \leq \Phi(T|f|)$ gives 3.1.5 for all f.

† Every function $\Phi(u)$ which has an integrable second derivative can be written in this form with $a = \Phi(0)$, $b = \Phi'(0)$, and $\varphi(\sigma) = \Phi''(\sigma)$. Thus 3.1.1 is merely a regularity assumption.

Note. It is worthwhile to point out that when $\Phi(u)$ is non-decreasing, the hypothesis 3.1.2(a) is not really essential. Its use can be avoided by starting with the inequality

$$(|Tf| - C)^+ \leq |T(f - C)^+| + |T(-f - C)^+|,$$

rather than with 3.1.3.

Proposition 3.1.1 of course applies to conditional expectation operators since they satisfy the requirements in 3.1.2. However, it is worthwhile to obtain the Jensen's inequalities directly in this case. To this end let us say that two functions f and g are in "martingale relation" if there is a Borel field $\mathscr{G}$ such that

3.1.6 (a) $\mathscr{F}(f) \subset \mathscr{G}$ [$\mathscr{F}(f)$ denotes the Borel field of f];

(b) $\displaystyle\int_\Lambda f\,d\mu = \int_\Lambda g\,d\mu \qquad \forall \quad \Lambda \in \mathscr{G}.$

We shall indicate this relation by writing $f \underset{\mathscr{G}}{\sim} g$.

Also if f and g are nonnegative and we have

3.1.7 (a) $\mathscr{F}(f) \subset \mathscr{G}$,

(b) $\displaystyle\int_\Lambda f\,d\mu \leq \int_\Lambda g\,d\mu \qquad \forall \quad \Lambda \in \mathscr{G},$

we shall write $f \underset{\mathscr{G}}{\lessdot} g$ and say that f and g are in submartingale relation.

Note that if $f \underset{\mathscr{G}}{\sim} g$, then $|f| \underset{\mathscr{G}}{\lessdot} |g|$. Indeed, for $\Lambda \in \mathscr{G}$,

$$\int_\Lambda f^+\,d\mu = \int_{\Lambda \cap \{f > 0\}} f\,d\mu = \int_{\Lambda \cap \{f > 0\}} g\,d\mu \leq \int_\Lambda g^+\,d\mu,$$

$$\int_\Lambda f^-\,d\mu = \int_{\Lambda \cap \{f < 0\}} -f\,d\mu = \int_{\Lambda \cap \{f < 0\}} -g\,d\mu \leq \int_\Lambda g^-\,d\mu.$$

Thus upon adding these inequalities we obtain

$$\int_\Lambda |f|\,d\mu \leq \int_\Lambda |g|\,d\mu \qquad \forall \quad \Lambda \in \mathscr{G}.$$

If $f \underset{\mathscr{G}}{\lessdot} g$ and $C > 0$, for all $\Lambda \in \mathscr{G}$ we get

$$\int_\Lambda (f - C)^+\,d\mu = \int_{\Lambda \cap \{f > C\}} (f - C)\,d\mu = \int_{\Lambda \cap \{f > C\}} (g - C)\,d\mu$$
$$\leq \int_\Lambda (g - C)^+\,d\mu.$$

And this is what corresponds here to 3.1.4. We can thus formulate

PROPOSITION 3.1.2. *If $\Phi(u)(\geq 0)$ is convex with $b \geq 0$ in 3.1.1 and $f \underset{\mathscr{G}}{\lessdot} g$, then*

3.1.8 $$\int_\Lambda \Phi(f)\,d\mu \leq \int_\Lambda \Phi(g)\,d\mu \qquad \forall \quad \Lambda \in \mathscr{G}.$$

In other words, we must also have $\Phi(f) \underset{\mathscr{G}}{\lessdot} \Phi(g)$. Furthermore, even if $\Phi(u)$ decreases somewhere, this remains true at least when $f, g \geq 0$ and $f \underset{\mathscr{G}}{\gtrapprox} g$.

Note. In case $\mu(\Omega) < \infty$, Proposition 3.1.2 with $f = E(g|\mathscr{G})$ and $g \geq 0$ gives

$$\Phi(E(g|\mathscr{G})) \leq E(\Phi(g)|\mathscr{G}),$$

for all convex $\Phi(u)$.

It will be helpful to obtain one more inequality before closing this section:

PROPOSITION 3.1.3. *If $\Phi(u) = \int_0^u (u - \sigma)\varphi(\sigma)\,d\sigma$ with $\varphi(\sigma) = \varphi(-\sigma) \geq 0$ and $\varphi(\sigma)$ is nonincreasing for $\sigma \geq 0$, then*

3.1.9 $$\tfrac{1}{8}\int_\Omega |f - g|^2 \varphi(|f| \vee |g|)\,d\mu \leq \int_\Omega \left[\Phi(f) + \Phi(g) - 2\Phi\left(\frac{f+g}{2}\right)\right] d\mu.\dagger$$

PROOF. We have for any $u_1 \leq (u_1 + u_2)/2 \leq u_2$,

$$\Phi(u_1) + \Phi(u_2) - 2\Phi\left(\frac{u_1 + u_2}{2}\right) = \int_{u_1}^{(u_1+u_2)/2} (\sigma - u_1)\varphi(\sigma)\,d\sigma + \int_{(u_1+u_2)/2}^{u_2} (u_2 - \sigma)\varphi(\sigma)\,d\sigma.$$

If $\varphi(\sigma)$ is nonincreasing,

$$\Phi(u_1) + \Phi(u_1) - 2\Phi\left(\frac{u_1 + u_2}{2}\right) \geq \varphi(u_2)\left(\frac{u_2 - u_1}{2}\right)^2 \frac{1}{2}.$$

† *When $\varphi(\sigma)$ is nondecreasing for $\sigma \geq 0$, we can get*

$$\tfrac{1}{8}\int_\Omega |f - g|^2 \varphi\left(\frac{f+g}{2}\right) d\mu \leq \int_\Omega \left\{\Phi(f) + \Phi(g) - 2\Phi\left(\frac{f+g}{2}\right)\right\} d\mu.$$

So without any restriction on u_1, u_2 we get

$$\Phi(u_1) + \Phi(u_2) - 2\Phi\left(\frac{u_1 + u_2}{2}\right) \geq \varphi(|u_1| \vee |u_2|)\left(\frac{u_2 - u_1}{2}\right)^2 \frac{1}{2}.$$

The inequality in 3.1.9 is thus obtained upon replacing u_1, u_2 by f and g, respectively, and integrating over Ω.

3.2 INEQUALITIES FOR MARTINGALES

The material in this section is included for the sake of completeness and also because it will help our understanding of the arguments which follow.

We recall that a martingale is a finite or infinite system $S_1, S_2, \ldots, S_n$ of functions such that for $m \geq l$,

3.2.1 $$\int_\Lambda S_l \, d\mu = \int_\Lambda S_m \, d\mu \qquad \forall \quad \Lambda \in \mathscr{F}(S_1, S_2, \ldots, S_l).$$

And a submartingale is a system of nonnegative functions $P_1, P_2, \ldots, P_n$ such that for $m \geq l$,

3.2.2 $$\int_\Lambda P_l \, d\mu \leq \int_\Lambda P_m \, d\mu \qquad \forall \quad \Lambda \in \mathscr{F}(P_1, P_2, \ldots, P_l).$$

From one of our remarks in the previous section we deduce that if $S_1, S_2, \ldots, S_n$ is a martingale, then $|S_1|, |S_2|, \ldots, |S_n|$ is a submartingale. We have the classical

PROPOSITION 3.2.1. *If $P_1, P_2, \ldots, P_n$ is a submartingale and we set $P_n^* = \max_{1 \leq \nu \leq n} P_\nu$, then for all $\lambda > 0$ we get*

3.2.3 $$\mu\{P_n^* > \lambda\} \leq \frac{1}{\lambda} \int_{\{P_n^* > \lambda\}} P_n \, d\mu \leq \frac{1}{\lambda} \int_\Omega P_n \, d\mu.$$

PROOF. We set $E = \{P_n^* > \lambda\}$, $E_l = \{P_1 \leq \lambda, \ldots, P_{l-1} \leq \lambda; P_l > \lambda\}$ for $l = 1, 2, \ldots, n$. Clearly $E_1, E_2, \ldots, E_n$ decompose E and $E_l \in \mathscr{F}(P_1, P_2, \ldots, P_l)$. So from 3.2.2 we obtain

$$\int_E P_n \, d\mu = \sum_{l=1}^{n} \int_{E_l} P_n \, d\mu \geq \sum_{l=1}^{n} \int_{E_l} P_l \, d\mu \geq \lambda \sum_{l=1}^{n} \mu(E_l) = \lambda\mu(E).$$

We can thus deduce

PROPOSITION 3.2.2. *If $\{P_n\}$ is a submartingale and*

$$\Lambda = \sup_n \int_\Omega P_n \, d\mu < \infty,$$

then for the function $P^* = \sup_n P_n$ we have

$$P^* < \infty \quad \text{a.e.}$$

A similar result then holds for $S^* = \sup_n |S_n|$, when $\{S_n\}$ is a martingale.

PROOF. Indeed, by passing to the limit as $n \to \infty$ in 3.2.3 we get for all $\lambda > 0$,

$$\mu\{P^* > \lambda\} \leq \frac{\Lambda}{\lambda}.$$

And this, of course, implies our assertion.

We are now in a position to present an interesting proof of the classical martingale theorem via an approach that we learned from E. Bishop.

Let $\{S_n\}$ be a martingale. Fixed m and $\epsilon > 0$, we would like to estimate the size of the set

$$F_m = \{\sup_{n \geq m} |S_n - S_m| > \epsilon\}.$$

To this end, for each $l \geq 0$ let

$$\mathcal{O}_l^* = \max_{0 \leq k \leq l} |S_{m+k} - S_m|, \; S^* = \sup_n |S_n|,$$

and set, for $k \geq 1$,

$$E_k = \{\mathcal{O}_{k-1}^* \leq \epsilon ; \mathcal{O}_k^* > \epsilon\} = \{\mathcal{O}_{k-1}^* \leq \epsilon ; |S_{m+k} - S_m| > \epsilon\}.$$

Define also, for $l \geq 1$,

$$T_l = \sum_{k=1}^{l} \chi_{E_k} S_{m+k} + \left(1 - \sum_{k=1}^{l} \chi_{E_k}\right) S_{m+l}.$$

We now apply Proposition 3.1.3, with $\Phi(u) = \int_0^u (u - \sigma) d\sigma/(1 + \sigma^2)$, to the functions $f = S_m$, $g = T_l$ and obtain

3.2.4 $$\frac{1}{8} \int_\Omega |T_l - S_m|^2 \frac{d\mu}{1 + (S^*)^2} \leq \int_\Omega \left[\Phi(T_l) + \Phi(S_m) - 2\Phi\left(\frac{T_l + S_m}{2}\right) \right] d\mu.$$

This estimate can be further simplified. In fact, note first that

$$\int_\Omega \Phi(T_l)\,d\mu = \sum_{k=1}^{l} \int_{E_k} \Phi(S_{m+k})\,d\mu + \int_{\Omega - \Sigma_{k=1}^{l} E_k} \Phi(S_{m+l})\,d\mu.$$

Then, using Proposition 3.1.2 and the relation $E_k \in \mathscr{F}(S_m, \dots, S_{m+k})$, we get

3.2.5
$$\int_\Omega \Phi(T_l)\,d\mu \le \sum_{k=1}^{l} \int_{E_k} \Phi(S_{m+l})\,d\mu + \int_{\Omega - \Sigma_{k=1}^{l} E_k} \Phi(S_{m+l})\,d\mu$$
$$= \int_\Omega \Phi(S_{m+l})\,d\mu.$$

On the other hand, for every $\Lambda \in \mathscr{F}(S_m)$ we have

$$\int_\Lambda T_l\,d\mu = \sum_{k=1}^{l} \int_{E_k \cap \Lambda} S_{m+k}\,d\mu + \int_{(\Omega - \Sigma_{k=1}^{l} E_k) \cap \Lambda} S_{m+l}\,d\mu$$
$$= \int_\Lambda S_{m+l}\,d\mu = \int_\Lambda S_m\,d\mu.$$

So we must also have

$$\int_\Lambda \frac{T_l + S_m}{2}\,d\mu = \int_\Lambda S_m\,d\mu \qquad \forall \quad \Lambda \in \mathscr{F}(S_m).$$

Thus, again by Proposition 3.1.2,

3.2.6
$$\int_\Omega \Phi(S_m)\,d\mu \le \int_\Omega \Phi\left(\frac{T_l + S_m}{2}\right)d\mu.$$

Substituting 3.2.5 and 3.2.6 in 3.2.4, from the definition of T_l we obtain

3.2.7
$$\sum_{k=1}^{l} \int_{E_k} |S_{m+k} - S_m|^2 \frac{d\mu}{1 + (S^*)^2}$$
$$\le \int_\Omega \Phi(S_{m+l})\,d\mu - \int_\Omega \Phi(S_m)\,d\mu.$$

We are now in a position to deduce

THE MARTINGALE THEOREM. *If* $\{S_n\}$ *is a martingale and* $\sup_n \int_\Omega |S_n|\,d\mu < \infty$, *then* $\{S_n\}$ *converges a.e.*

PROOF. Since

$$\Phi(u) = \int_0^u (u - \sigma)\frac{d\sigma}{1 + \sigma^2} \leq u \int_0^\infty \frac{d\sigma}{1 + \sigma^2},$$

we must also have, for this choice of $\Phi(u)$:

$$\Lambda = \sup_n \int_\Omega \Phi(S_n)\, d\mu < \infty.$$

By the definition of F_m and E_k, letting $l \to \infty$ in 3.2.7 we get

3.2.8 $$\epsilon^2 \int_{F_m} \frac{d\mu}{1 + (S^*)^2} = \epsilon^2 \sum_{k=1}^\infty \int_{E_k} \frac{d\mu}{1 + (S^*)^2} \leq \Lambda - \int_\Omega \Phi(S_m)\, d\mu.$$

By Proposition 3.2.2 $S^* < \infty$ a.e., and thus since 3.2.8 gives

$$\lim_{m\to\infty} \int_{F_m} \frac{d\mu}{1 + (S^*)^2} = 0,$$

we must also have

$$\lim_{m\to\infty} \mu\{F_m\} = \lim_{m\to\infty} \mu\{\sup_{n\geq m} |S_n - S_m| > \epsilon = 0\}.$$

However, the function $\sup_{n\geq m} |S_m - S_n|$ does not increase with m, so we must deduce that

$$\lim_{m\to\infty} \sup_{n\geq m} |S_m - S_n| = 0 \quad \text{a.e.}$$

This establishes our assertion.

3.3 YET ANOTHER PROOF OF THE MARTINGALE THEOREM

Recently another approach to the martingale convergence theorem was discovered by Isaac [21] and quite independently by L. Baez-Duarte.† This approach is also based upon the convexity inequalities of the last two sections, so we are in a position to present it in its entirety.

The argument can be broken down into three basic steps.

1. One first proves convergence result for submartingales $\{P_n\}$ having the property $\sup_n \int_\Omega P_n^2\, d\mu < \infty$.

2. We then get convergence for nonnegative martingales $\{S_n\}$ by observing that in that case the sequence $P_n = e^{-S_n}$ is a submartingale.

† Personal communication.

3. Finally, one shows that if $\{S_n\}$ is a martingale and $\sup_n \int_\Omega |S_n|\, d\mu < \infty$, then $\{S_n\}$ can be written as a difference of two nonnegative martingales having the same property.

The following propositions show how these steps can be carried out.

PROPOSITION 3.3.1. *Let $\{S_n\}$ be a martingale and suppose that $\sup_n \int_\Omega S_n^2\, d\mu < \infty$; then*

$$\lim_{n\to\infty} S_n$$

exists a.e.

PROOF. From the parallelogram law† we get for $n \geq m$

$$\int_\Omega (S_n - S_m)^2\, d\mu \leq \int_\Omega S_n^2\, d\mu + \int_\Omega S_m^2\, d\mu - 2\int_\Omega \left(\frac{S_n + S_m}{2}\right)^2 d\mu.$$

On the other hand, since $\forall\ \Lambda \in \mathscr{F}(S_m)$,

$$\int_\Lambda S_m\, d\mu = \int_\Lambda \frac{S_m + S_n}{2}\, d\mu,$$

we must have (Proposition 3.1.2)

$$\int_\Omega S_m^2\, d\mu \leq \int_\Omega \left(\frac{S_m + S_n}{2}\right)^2 d\mu.$$

Thus

$$\int_\Omega (S_n - S_m)^2\, d\mu \leq \int_\Omega S_n^2\, d\mu - \int_\Omega S_m^2\, d\mu.$$

Since the quantities $\int_\Omega S_n^2\, d\mu$ can only increase as $n \to \infty$ we get

$$\lim_{n,m\to\infty} \int_\Omega (S_n - S_m)^2\, d\mu = 0.$$

It is thus possible to choose a sequence $\{n_k\}$ such that

3.3.1

(a) $\displaystyle\sum_{k=1}^{\infty} \int_\Omega (S_{n_{k+1}} - S_{n_k})^2\, d\mu < \infty$;

(b) $\{S_{n_k}\}$ is almost everywhere convergent.

Proposition 3.2.1 for the submartingale

$$P_1 = (S_{n_k+1} - S_{n_k})^2, \ldots, P_n = (S_{n_k+n} - S_{n_k})^2 \qquad (n = n_{k+1} - n_k)$$

† Proposition 3.1.3 with $\Phi(u) = u^2/2$ would actually be sufficient here.

gives for any $\epsilon > 0$,

$$\mu\{\max_{n_k < m \leq n_{k+1}} (S_m - S_{n_k})^2 > \epsilon\} \leq \frac{1}{\epsilon^2} \int_\Omega (S_{n_{k+1}} - S_{n_k})^2 \, d\mu.$$

From 3.3.1(a) we then get that

$$\sum_{k=1}^{\infty} \mu\{\max_{n_k < m \leq n_{k+1}} |S_m - S_{n_k}|^2 > \epsilon\} < \infty,$$

and so for any $\epsilon > 0$ almost everywhere the inequality

$$\max_{n_k < m \leq n_{k+1}} |S_m - S_{n_k}|^2 > \epsilon$$

can only occur finitely many times. This combined with 3.3.1(b) establishes our assertion.

In the next few lines we shall need to use the operation of conditional expectation; for this reason it will be convenient to assume $\mu(\Omega) < \infty$. This is not a crucial restriction for the proof of the martingale theorem. Indeed, once the convergence result is obtained for the case $\mu(\Omega) < \infty$ to extend the result to the case $\mu(\Omega) = \infty$ one can proceed as follows. We start with a martingale $\{S_n\}$ for which $\sup_n \int_\Omega |S_n| \, d\mu < \infty$. Then we introduce the martingale

$$Y_n = S_n \chi_A$$

for a set $A = \{|S_1| > \epsilon\}$. Since $\mu(A) < \infty$, we are reduced to the finite measure case and thus conclude that $\{Y_n\}$ is a.e. convergent and therefore that $\{S_n\}$ is a.e. convergent in A. If we let $\epsilon \to 0$ we deduce the convergence on the set $\{|S_1| > 0\}$. To complete the argument we repeat this process with $S_2, S_3, \ldots$ replacing S_1.

Let, then, $\mu(\Omega) < \infty$.

PROPOSITION 3.3.2. *If $\{P_n\}$ is any sequence of integrable functions whatever, the functions*

3.3.2 $$S_n = P_n + \sum_{\nu=1}^{n-1} \{P_\nu - E(P_{\nu+1}|\mathscr{F}_\nu)\} \qquad (\mathscr{F}_\nu = \mathscr{F}(P_1, P_2, \ldots, P_\nu))$$

always form a martingale. Further, if $\{P_n\}$ is a submartingale, the sequence

$$Z_n = \sum_{\nu=1}^{n-1} \{E(P_{\nu+1}|\mathscr{F}_\nu) - P_\nu\} = P_n - S_n$$

is nonnegative, nondecreasing, and

3.3.3 $$\int_\Omega Z_n \, d\mu \le \int_\Omega P_n \, d\mu.$$

Finally when the P_n's are in L_2, we also have

3.3.4 $$\int_\Omega S_n^2 \, d\mu \le \int_\Omega P_n^2 \, d\mu.$$

PROOF. If $\Lambda \in \mathscr{F}(S_1, S_2, \ldots, S_n)$, then a fortiori $\Lambda \in \mathscr{F}(P_1, P_2, \ldots, P_n) = \mathscr{F}_n$. Since by our definition 3.3.2,

3.3.5 $$S_{n+1} = S_n + P_{n+1} - E(P_{n+1}|\mathscr{F}_n),$$

we must then have

$$\int_\Lambda S_{n+1} \, d\mu = \int_\Lambda S_n \, d\mu.$$

Thus $\{S_n\}$ is a martingale.

Further, if $\{P_n\}$ is a submartingale, then

$$P_\nu \le E(P_{\nu+1}|\mathscr{F}_\nu) \qquad \forall \quad \nu \ge 1,$$

and so in this case $\{Z_n\}$ is clearly nonnegative and nondecreasing. The inequality in 3.3.3 follows immediately upon integrating Z_n. As for 3.3.4, note that since S_n is measurable with regard to $\mathscr{F}_n$,

$$\int_\Omega S_n E(P_{n+1}|\mathscr{F}_n) \, d\mu = \int_\Omega E(S_n P_{n+1}|\mathscr{F}_n) \, d\mu = \int_\Omega S_n P_{n+1} \, d\mu.$$

So the terms S_n and $P_{n+1} - E(P_{n+1}|\mathscr{F}_n)$ are orthogonal; therefore, from 3.3.5 we get

$$\int_\Omega S_{n+1}^2 \, d\mu = \int_\Omega S_n^2 \, d\mu + \int_\Omega P_{n+1}^2 \, d\mu - \int_\Omega [E(P_{n+1}|\mathscr{F}_n)]^2 \, d\mu.\dagger$$

Using the fact that $\{P_n\}$ is a submartingale we deduce

$$\int_\Omega S_{n+1}^2 \, d\mu \le \int_\Omega S_n^2 \, d\mu + \int_\Omega P_{n+1}^2 \, d\mu - \int_\Omega P_n^2 \, d\mu.$$

Then 3.3.4 necessarily follows.

† This is because for any f and $\mathscr{B}$, $[E(f|\mathscr{B})]^2 = E(fE(f|\mathscr{B})|\mathscr{B})$ and so

$$\int_\Omega [f - E(f|\mathscr{B})]^2 \, d\mu = \int_\Omega f^2 \, d\mu - \int_\Omega [E(f|\mathscr{B})]^2 \, d\mu.$$

We are now in a position to prove

PROPOSITION 3.3.3. *If* $\{P_n\}$ *is a submartingale and* $\sup_n \int_\Omega P_n^2 \, d\mu < \infty$, *then*

$$\lim_{n \to \infty} P_n$$

exists a.e.

PROOF. By Proposition 3.3.2 we can write P_n in the form

$$P_n = S_n + Z_n.$$

Since $\{Z_n\}$ is nonnegative and nondecreasing, and by 3.3.3

$$\int_\Omega Z_n \, d\mu \le \int_\Omega P_n \, d\mu \le \left(\int_\Omega P_n^2 \, d\mu \right)^{1/2} \sqrt{\mu(\Omega)},$$

the sequence $\{Z_n\}$ is convergent a.e.

Further, since $\{S_n\}$ is a martingale and 3.3.4 holds, by Proposition 3.3.1, $\{S_n\}$ must be almost everywhere convergent as well. So our proposition is established.

As a corollary we obtain the following remarkable

PROPOSITION 3.3.4. *If* $\{S_n\}$ *is a nonnegative martingale, then the sequence*

$$P_n = e^{-S_n}$$

is almost everywhere convergent. This means that almost everywhere the sequence $\{S_n\}$ *is either convergent to a finite quantity or diverges to infinity. In particular, if* $\sup_n \int_\Omega |S_n| \, d\mu < \infty$, *the sequence* $\{S_n\}$ *must be almost everywhere convergent.*

PROOF. By Proposition 3.1.2 the sequence $P_n = e^{-S_n}$ is a submartingale. Since $S_n \ge 0$ this sequence is bounded. Thus Proposition 3.3.3 applies, and we deduce that e^{-S_n} must converge almost everywhere. If, in addition, we know that $\sup_n \int_\Omega |S_n| \, d\mu < \infty$, then from Proposition 3.2.2 we get that $\{S_n\}$ can diverge to ∞ only on a set of measure zero; and therefore $\{S_n\}$ must be almost everywhere convergent.

To obtain the second proof of the martingale theorem we need only show the following

PROPOSITION 3.3.5. *If* $\{S_n\}$ *is a martingale and* $\sup_n \int_\Omega |S_n| \, d\mu < \infty$, *then the sequence*

$$P_n = |S_n| + \sum_{\nu = n}^{\infty} E(|S_{\nu+1}| - |S_\nu| \,|\, \mathscr{F}_n) \qquad (\mathscr{F}_n = \mathscr{F}(S_1, S_2, \ldots, S_n))$$

is a martingale. Further we have

3.3.6
$$\text{(a)}\ |S_n| \le P_n;$$
$$\text{(b)}\ \int_\Omega |P_n|\,d\mu \le \sup_n \int_\Omega |S_n|\,d\mu.$$

Therefore, if we write

$$S_n = P_n - (P_n - S_n)$$

we obtain a decomposition of S_n into the difference of two nonnegative martingales, with bounded L_1 norms.

PROOF. Note that for each ν,

$$E(|S_{\nu+1}| \mid \mathscr{F}_\nu) \ge |S_\nu|.$$

And therefore, for $n \le \nu$,

$$E(|S_{\nu+1}| \mid \mathscr{F}_n) \ge E(|S_\nu| \mid \mathscr{F}_n).$$

Thus, for fixed n the sequence

$$Q_N^{(n)} = |S_n| + \sum_{\nu=n}^{N} E(|S_{\nu+1}| - |S_\nu| \mid \mathscr{F}_n) = E(|S_{N+1}| \mid \mathscr{F}_n)$$

is nonnegative and nondecreasing. Further we have

$$\int_\Omega Q_N^{(n)}\,d\mu = \int_\Omega |S_{N+1}|\,d\mu.$$

Under the hypothesis

$$A = \sup_n \int_\Omega |S_n|\,d\mu < \infty,$$

by the monotone convergence theorem $Q_N^{(n)}$ has a limit as $N \to \infty$; its limit

$$P_n = |S_n| + \sum_{\nu=n}^{\infty} E(|S_{\nu+1}| - |S_\nu| \mid \mathscr{F}_n)$$

is in L_1 and

3.3.7
$$\int_\Omega P_n\,d\mu \le A.$$

Finally, if $\Lambda \in \mathscr{F}(P_1, P_2, \ldots, P_{n-1})$, then a fortiori $\Lambda \in \mathscr{F}_{n-1}$; so then

$$\int_\Lambda Q_N^{(n)}\, d\mu = \int_\Lambda E(|S_{N+1}| \,|\, \mathscr{F}_n)\, d\mu = \int_\Lambda E(|S_{N+1}| \,|\, \mathscr{F}_{n-1})\, d\mu$$

$$= \int_\Lambda Q_N^{(n-1)}\, d\mu.$$

Passing to the limit as $N \to \infty$,

$$\int_\Lambda P_n\, d\mu = \int_\Lambda P_{n-1}\, d\mu \qquad \forall \quad \Lambda \in \mathscr{F}(P_1, P_2, \ldots, P_{n-1}).$$

This establishes that $\{P_n\}$ is a martingale. Property 3.3.6(a) follows trivially, since each term $E(|S_{\nu+1}| - |S_\nu| \,|\, \mathscr{F}_n)$ is nonnegative. Thus our proof is complete.

3.4 SOME WELL-BEHAVED ORTHONORMAL SYSTEMS

Let as before $(\Omega, \mathscr{F}, \mu)$ denote a finite or infinite measure space and let $\{\Phi_n\}$ be orthonormal in $L_2(\Omega, \mathscr{F}, \mu)$. In other words, we assume that

$$\int_\Omega \Phi_i \Phi_j\, d\mu = \delta_{ij} \qquad i, j = 1, 2, \ldots.$$

For a given $f \in L_2$ we write

$$S_n(x, f) = \sum_{\nu=1}^{n} a_\nu \Phi_\nu(x) \qquad \left(\text{with } a_\nu = \int_\Omega \Phi_\nu f\, d\mu\right),$$

$$S_n^*(x, f) = \max_{1 \le \nu \le n} |S_\nu(x, f)|,$$

$$S^*(x, f) = \sup_n S_n^*(x, f).$$

Bessel's inequality gives

$$a_1^2 + a_2^2 + \cdots + a_n^2 = \int_\Omega S_n^2(x, f)\, d\mu \le \int_\Omega |f|^2\, d\mu, \tag{3.4.1}$$

and we know that

$$\lim_{n \to \infty} \int_\Omega |S_n(x, f) - f|^2\, d\mu = 0 \tag{3.4.2}$$

if and only if

$$\sum_{\nu=1}^{\infty} a_\nu^2 = \int_\Omega |f|^2 \, d\mu.$$

Thus $\{S_n(x, f)\}$ is always bounded in the L_2 sense. So by Proposition 3.3.1 we can be sure that $S_n(x, f)$ will converge a.e. (and to f if 3.4.2 is satisfied) whenever $\{S_n(x, f)\}$ is a martingale.

It is easy to see that the sequence $\{S_n(x, f)\}$ is a martingale for all $f \in L_2$, or equivalently the sequence

$$S_n(x, a) = \sum_{\nu=1}^{n} a_\nu \Phi_\nu(x)$$

is a martingale for all $a = (a_1, a_2, \ldots, a_n, \ldots)$ with $\sum_{\nu=1}^{\infty} a_\nu^2 < \infty$, if and only if

3.4.3 $$\int_\Lambda \Phi_{n+1} \, d\mu = 0 \qquad \forall \;\; n \geq 1 \;\text{ and }\; \forall \;\; \Lambda \in \mathscr{F}(\Phi_1, \Phi_2, \ldots, \Phi_n).$$

Here, as customary, $\mathscr{F}(\Phi_1, \Phi_2, \ldots, \Phi_n)$ denotes the least Borel field with respect to which $\Phi_1, \Phi_2, \ldots, \Phi_n$ are measurable.

Systems $\{\Phi_n\}$ satisfying condition 3.4.3 are called *systems of martingale differences*. The behavior of expansions in terms of such systems has recently been studied extensively by Gundy [15]; here we shall only present some of the most basic facts.

The simplest examples of systems of martingale differences are obtained by taking a sequence of independent square-integrable random variables $\{X_n\}$ on a probability space $(\Omega, \mathscr{F}, P)$ and setting

$$\Phi_n = \frac{X_n - \mu_n}{\sigma_n},$$

where

$$\mu_n = \int_\Omega X_n \, dP, \qquad \sigma_n = \sqrt{\int_\Omega X_n^2 \, dP - \mu_n^2}.$$

In fact, the Φ_n's have clearly norm one. Further, because of the independence of $X_1, X_2, \ldots, X_n$ for any $\Lambda \in \mathscr{F}(\Phi_1, \Phi_2, \ldots, \Phi_n)$, the functions χ_Λ and Φ_{n+1} are independent, so then

$$\int_\Lambda \Phi_{n+1} \, dP = \int_\Omega \chi_\Lambda \Phi_{n+1} \, dP = \left(\int_\Omega \chi_\Lambda \, dP\right)\left(\int_\Omega \Phi_{n+1} \, dP\right) = 0.$$

So condition 3.4.3 holds in this case and in addition the Φ_n's form an orthonormal system.

This given we can start by formalizing our remarks above by the following

PROPOSITION 3.4.1. *If $\{\Phi_n\}$ is an orthogonal system of martingale differences, in particular, if the Φ_n's are independent random variables with mean zero and square integral one, then the expansions*

$$S_n(x, f) = \sum_{\nu=1}^{n} a_\nu \Phi_\nu(x) \qquad \left(a_\nu = \int_\Omega f \Phi_\nu \, d\mu\right)$$

converge a.e. for all $f \in L_2(\Omega, \mathscr{F}, \mu)$. Further, combining Proposition 3.2.1, *with Theorem* 2.2.3, *we also get in this case*

3.4.4 $$\int_\Omega [S_n^*(x, f)]^2 \, d\mu \leq 4 \int_\Omega |f|^2 \, d\mu.$$

Two classical examples of systems to which this result applies are the Rademacher and the Haar systems. These are both defined on [0, 1] and orthonormal with respect to Lebesgue measure.

The Rademacher system $\{R_n\}$ is defined as follows. We set $R_0(x) = 1$ for $0 \leq x \leq 1$. For $n \geq 1$, we expand each $x \in [0, 1)$ in a binary series

$$x = \sum_{n=1}^{\infty} \frac{a_n}{2^n}$$

with $a_n = \begin{Bmatrix} 0 \\ 1 \end{Bmatrix}$ (expansions terminating with a string of ones are excluded), then set

$$R_n(x) = 2a_n - 1.$$

It is easily verified that these functions are independent and that

$$\int_0^1 R_n^2 \, dx = 1, \qquad \int_0^1 R_n \, dx = 0 \qquad \forall \quad n \geq 1.$$

The Haar system arises in a natural way [15] if we try to seek systems of martingale differences that are complete. In fact, suppose that a given system Φ_n on a finite measure space $(\Omega, \mathscr{F}, \mu)$ satisfies 3.4.3 and in addition is complete. Then for every $f \in L_2$ we must have

$$\int_\Omega |S_n(x, f) - f(x)|^2 \, d\mu \to 0 \qquad \text{as } n \to \infty.$$

So, in particular for any $\Lambda \in \mathscr{F}(\Phi_1, \Phi_2, \ldots, \Phi_n)$

$$\lim_{m \to \infty} \int_\Lambda S_m(x, f)\, d\mu = \int_\Lambda f(x)\, d\mu.$$

However, by condition 3.4.3 we deduce then that

$$\int_\Lambda S_n(x, f)\, d\mu = \int_\Lambda f\, d\mu.$$

In other words, we must have

$$E(f \mid \Phi_1, \Phi_2, \ldots, \Phi_n) = S_n(x, f) = a_1\Phi_1 + a_2\Phi_2 + \cdots + a_n\Phi_n.$$

We thus deduce that the class of functions of $\Phi_1, \Phi_2, \ldots, \Phi_n$ is linear and n-dimensional. It is easy to see that this is the case if and only if the field of $\Phi_1, \Phi_2, \ldots, \Phi_n$ has exactly n atoms. This implies that for each n the field $\mathscr{F}(\Phi_1, \Phi_2, \ldots, \Phi_{n+1})$ can be obtained from $\mathscr{F}(\Phi_1, \Phi_2, \ldots, \Phi_n)$ by splitting one of the atoms in two. In other words, Φ_{n+1} should be constant on each of the atoms of $\mathscr{F}(\Phi_1, \Phi_2, \ldots, \Phi_n)$ with the exception of one in which it takes two different values.

If we try to follow the above recipe on $[0, 1]$ in the simplest way we come up with the Haar system. More precisely, the Haar functions $\{H_n(x)\}$, $n = 0, 1, 2, \ldots$, can be defined as follows. The first two are the same as the Rademacher functions R_0, R_1. For $n \geq 2$ we write

$$n = 1 + 2 + \cdots + 2^{\nu-2} + \lambda$$

with $\nu \geq 2$ and $1 \leq \lambda \leq 2^{\nu-1}$. We then set

$$H_n(x) = \begin{cases} \sqrt{2^{\nu-1}}\, R_\nu(x) & \text{for } \dfrac{2\lambda - 2}{2^\nu} \leq x < \dfrac{2\lambda}{2^\nu}, \\ 0 & \text{otherwise.} \end{cases}$$

(The factor $\sqrt{2^{\nu-1}}$ is necessary to get the proper normalization.) Property 3.4.3 for $\{H_n(x)\}$ can be immediately verified.

A complete system of martingale differences has some additional desirable properties. For simplicity we shall state these properties for the Haar system.

Note that since the H_n's are bounded functions we can introduce $S_n(x, f)$ for every $f \in L_p$ $(p \geq 1)$; in addition,

$$S_n(x, f) = E(f \mid H_0, H_1, \ldots, H_n);$$

therefore, in this case we must also have [by Proposition 3.1.2 with $\Phi(u) = |u|^p$]

$$\int_0^1 |S_n(x, f)|^p \, dx \leq \int_0^1 |f|^p \, dx.$$

Combining these facts with Proposition 3.2.1 and Theorem 2.2.3 we obtain

THEOREM 3.4.1. *If $\{H_n(x)\}$ denotes the Haar system and for every $f \in L_p(0, 1)$ $(p \geq 1)$ we write*

$$S_n(x, f) = \sum_{\nu=0}^{n} a_\nu H_\nu(x), \qquad a_\nu = \int_0^1 H_\nu(x) f(x) \, dx$$

then

$$S_n(x, f) \to f(x) \quad \text{a.e.}$$

Further, for $p > 1$, $S^*(x, f) = \sup|S_n(x, f)|$ is in L_p when $f \in L_p$ and

3.4.5 $$\int_0^1 [S^*(x, f)]^p \, dx \leq \left(\frac{p}{p-1}\right)^p \int_0^1 |f(x)|^p \, dx.$$

Remarks. The inequalities in 3.4.4 and 3.4.5 in addition to convergence almost everywhere are a rather interesting fact. Indeed, it is not difficult to deduce from the continuity principle that for the partial sums of classical Fourier series

$$S_n(x, f) = a_0 + \sum_{\nu=1}^{n} (a_\nu \cos \nu x + b_\nu \sin \nu x)_{\sigma_\nu}^{a_\nu} = \frac{1}{\pi} \int_{-\pi}^{\pi} f(x)_{\sin}^{\cos} \nu x \, dx,$$

the a.e. convergence result $\forall f \in L_2(-\pi, \pi)$ is equivalent to an inequality such as

$$\int_{-\pi}^{\pi} S^*(x, f) \, dx \leq C\left(\int_{-\pi}^{\pi} |f|^2 \, dx\right)^{1/2} \qquad \forall \; f \in L_2.$$

However, the methods of Chapter 1 stop just short of giving

3.4.6 $$\int_{-\pi}^{\pi} [S^*(x, f)]^2 \, dx \leq C \int_{-\pi}^{\pi} |f|^2 \, dx.$$

Nevertheless, more recently Hunt [20] was able to show that inequalities such as 3.4.5 and 3.4.6 hold also for the Fourier system. Hunt's methods are essentially a modification of Carleson's.

It is not difficult to show that orthonormal systems made up of independent random variables are generally not complete. Further yet, sums of independent random variables being either very good or very bad, it is natural to infer that only relatively good functions admit a representation in term of such systems. This is indeed the case. In the next section we shall present some classical inequalities we shall need in the sequel and at the same time obtain a more precise expression of this fact.

3.5 L_p ESTIMATES FOR SUMS OF INDEPENDENT RANDOM VARIABLES

In this section we shall obtain certain classical estimates for integrals of the form

$$I_p = \int_\Omega |a_1 X_1 + a_2 X_2 + \cdots + a_n X_n|^p \, dP$$

when $X_1, X_2, \ldots, X_n$ are independent random variables on a probability space $(\Omega, \mathscr{F}, P)$. Here $(a_1, a_2, \ldots, a_n)$ denote real constants.

It is instructive to study I_p in special cases first. Let $\xi_1, \xi_2, \ldots, \xi_n$ denote independent Gaussian variables with mean zero and variance one.† In other words, we are requiring that

$$P(\xi_1 \leq \alpha_1, \xi_2 \leq \alpha_2, \ldots, \xi_n \leq \alpha_n) = \int_{-\infty}^{\alpha_1} \int_{-\infty}^{\alpha_2} \cdots \int_{-\infty}^{\alpha_n} e^{-(x_1^2 + \cdots + x_n^2)/2} \frac{dx_1 \, dx_2 \cdots dx_n}{(2\pi)^{n/2}}.$$

This given, it is easy to calculate I_p when $X_i = \xi_i$ $(i = 1, 2, \ldots, n)$. Indeed then the variable

$$\xi = a_1 \xi_1 + a_2 \xi_2 + \cdots + a_n \xi_n$$

has also a Gaussian distribution and has mean zero. Further, its variance is

$$a_1^2 + a_2^2 + \cdots + a_n^2.$$

We must therefore have in this case

$$I_p = \int_\Omega |a_1 \xi_1 + a_2 \xi_2 + \cdots + a_n \xi_n|^p \, dP = (a_1^2 + a_2^2 + \cdots + a_n^2)^{p/2} \int_{-\infty}^{+\infty} |x|^p e^{-x^2/2} \frac{dx}{\sqrt{2\pi}}.$$

† We recall that if X is a random variable, the mean of X is $\int_\Omega X \, dP$ and the variance is $\int_\Omega X^2 \, dP - (\int_\Omega X \, dP)^2$.

An elementary calculation gives

$$\int_{-\infty}^{+\infty} x^{2p} e^{-x^2/2} \frac{dx}{\sqrt{2\pi}} = (2p-1)(2p-3) \cdots 3.1 = \frac{(2p)!}{2^p p!}.$$

Thus for even integral exponents $2p$ we get

3.5.1 $$I_{2p} = (a_1^2 + a_2^2 + \cdots + a_n^2)^p \frac{(2p)!}{2^p p!}$$

$$= \frac{(2p)!}{2^p p!} \left(\int_\Omega |a_1\xi_1 + a_2\xi_2 + \cdots + a_n\xi_n|^2 \, dP \right)^p.$$

In other words, we can estimate the L_{2p} norm of $a_1\xi_1 + a_2\xi_2 + \cdots + a_n\xi_n$ for any integer $p \geq 1$ in terms of the L_2 norm. This remarkable fact is not peculiar of the Gaussian case but it holds quite generally.

The simplest case to work with is when $X_1, X_2, \ldots, X_n$, in addition to being in L_{2p}, satisfy the condition.

3.5.2 $$\int_\Omega X_1^{\alpha_1} X_2^{\alpha_2} \cdots X_n^{\alpha_n} \, dP = 0 \qquad \text{when at least one } \alpha_i \text{ is odd.}$$

It is easily verified that this condition holds for instance when $X_1, X_2, \ldots, X_n$ are independent and symmetrically distributed; that is, for each $i = 1, 2, \ldots, n$,

$$P\{X_i \geq a\} = P\{X_i \leq -a\} \qquad \forall \quad a \geq 0.$$

Indeed this condition is sufficient to imply that all odd moments vanish.

The estimates are as follows.

PROPOSITION 3.5.1. *If $X_1, X_2, \ldots, X_n$ are in L_{2p} and satisfy the condition 3.5.2, then*

3.5.3 $$I_{2p} = \int_\Omega |a_1X_1 + a_2X_2 + \cdots + a_nX_n|^{2p} \, dP$$

$$\leq \frac{(2p)!}{2^p p!} M^{2p} (a_1^2 + a_2^2 + \cdots + a_n^2)^p,$$

where $M = \max_{1 \leq \nu \leq n} (\int_\Omega X_\nu^{2p} \, d\mu)^{1/2p}$. In particular, 3.5.3, holds when $X_1, X_2, \ldots, X_n$ are independent and symmetrically distributed.

PROOF. We can write I_{2p} in the form

$$I_{2p} = \sum_{\alpha_1+\alpha_2+\cdots+\alpha_n=2p} \frac{(2p)!}{\alpha_1!\cdots\alpha_n!}\int_\Omega X_1^{\alpha_1}\cdots X_n^{\alpha_n}\,dP\, a_1^{\alpha_1}\cdots a_n^{\alpha_n}.$$

Note that by Holder's inequality

$$\int_\Omega X_1^{\alpha_1}\cdots X_n^{\alpha_n}\,dP \le \left(\int_\Omega X_2^{2p}\,dP\right)^{\alpha_1/2p}\cdots\left(\int_\Omega X_n^{2p}\,dP\right)^{\alpha_n/2p} \le M^{2p}.$$

Thus, in view of the hypothesis 3.5.2 for all $\alpha_1 + \cdots + \alpha_n = 2p$ we have

$$\int_\Omega X_1^{\alpha_1}\cdots X_n^{\alpha_n}\,dP \le M^{2p}\int_\Omega \xi_1^{\alpha_1}\cdots\xi_n^{\alpha_n}\,dP.$$

where $\xi_1, \xi_2,\ldots, \xi_n$ are the Gaussian variables introduced at the beginning of this section. We thus obtain

$$I_{2p} = \int_\Omega |a_1X_1 + a_2X_2 + \cdots + a_nX_n|^{2p}\,dP$$

$$\le M^{2p}\int_\Omega |a_1\xi_1 + \cdots + a_n\xi_n|^{2p}\,dP.$$

Therefore, 3.5.3 follows from 3.5.1.

With a slight loss in the constants these inequalities can be established by assuming only independence. The idea consists in reducing the general case to the symmetric case. We start with $X_1(\omega), X_2(\omega),\ldots, X_n(\omega)$ being given independent random variables on a probability space $(\Omega, \mathscr{F}, P)$, then introduce two identical copies $(\Omega_1, \mathscr{F}_1, P_1)$ and $(\Omega_2, \mathscr{F}_2, P_2)$ of $(\Omega, \mathscr{F}, P)$ and work with the variables

$$Z_\nu(\omega_1, \omega_2) = X_\nu(\omega_1) - X_\nu(\omega_2) \qquad \nu = 1, 2,\ldots, n$$

as ω_1 and ω_2 vary in Ω_1 and Ω_2, respectively. It is easy to see that $Z_1, Z_2,\ldots, Z_n$ will be independent and in L_p if $X_1, X_2,\ldots, X_n$ are such. However, $Z_1, Z_2,\ldots, Z_n$ are automatically symmetric.

An application of Proposition 3.5.1 then gives

3.5.4
$$\int_{\Omega_1}\int_{\Omega_2} |A(\omega_1) - A(\omega_2)|^{2p}\,dP_1\,dP_2 \le \frac{(2p)!}{2^p p!}N^{2p}(a_1^2 + \cdots + a_n^2)^p,$$

where we have set

$$A(\omega) = a_1 X_1(\omega) + \cdots + a_n X_n(\omega)$$

and

$$N = \max_{1 \le \nu \le n} \left\{ \int_{\Omega_1} \int_{\Omega_2} |X_\nu(\omega_1) - X_\nu(\omega_2)|^{2p} \, dP_1 \, dP_2 \right\}^{1/2p}$$

$$\le 2 \max_{1 \le \nu \le n} \left(\int_\Omega |X_\nu|^{2p} \, dP \right)^{1/2p}.$$

We then note that Jensen's inequality gives for any $\omega_1 \in \Omega_1$,

$$|A(\omega_1) - \int_{\Omega_2} A(\omega_2) \, dP_2|^{2p} \le \int_{\Omega_2} |A(\omega_1) - A(\omega_2)|^{2p} \, dP_2.$$

Integrating over Ω_1 we get

3.5.5 $$\int_{\Omega_1} |A(\omega_1) - \int_{\Omega_2} A(\omega_2) \, dP_2|^{2p} \, dP_1 \le \int_{\Omega_1} \int_{\Omega_2} |A(\omega_1) - A(\omega_2)|^{2p} \, dP_1 \, dP_2.$$

Combining 3.5.4 and 3.5.5 we easily deduce

PROPOSITION 3.5.2. *If $X_1, X_2, \ldots, X_n$ are independent, have zero mean, and are in L_{2p} (p integer ≥ 1), then if we set $M = \max_{1 \le \nu \le n} (\int_\Omega X_\nu^{2p} \, dP)^{1/2p}$ for all real $(a_1, a_2, \ldots, a_n)$ we have*

3.5.6 $$\int_\Omega |a_1 X_1 + a_2 X_2 + \cdots + a_n X_n|^{2p} \, dP \le \frac{2^p (2p)!}{p!} M^{2p} (a_1^2 + \cdots + a_n^2)^p.$$

From this result we immediately obtain the following suggestive

PROPOSITION 3.5.3. *If $Y_1, Y_2, \ldots, Y_n$ are independent, have zero mean, and are in L_{2p} (p integer ≥ 1), then we have*

$$\| Y_1 + Y_2 + \cdots + Y_n \|_{2p} \le \sqrt{2} \left[\frac{(2p)!}{p!} \right]^{1/2p} M \| Y_1 + \cdots + Y_n \|_2,$$

where

$$M = \max_{1 \le \nu \le n} \frac{\| Y_\nu \|_{2p}}{\| Y_\nu \|_2}.$$

When $X_1, X_2, \ldots, X_n$ are bounded and

$$|X_\nu| \leq M \qquad \text{for } \nu = 1, 2, \ldots, n,$$

the inequality 3.5.6 holds for all integers p. In this case if we multiply it by $(1/p!)(C/8)^p$ and sum we obtain

$$\int_\Omega e^{(C/8)|a_1 X_1 + \cdots + a_n X_n|^2}\, dP \leq \sum_{p=0}^{\infty} \{M^2 C(a_1^2 + \cdots + a_n^2)\}^p \frac{(2p)!}{(2^p p!)^2}.$$

Or, better,

$$\int_\Omega e^{(C/8)|a_1 X_1 + \cdots + a_n X_n|^2}\, dP \leq \frac{1}{\sqrt{1 - M^2 C(a_1^2 + \cdots + a_n^2)}}.$$

By choosing $C = 1/2M^2(a_1^2 + \cdots + a_n^2)$ we finally get

3.5.7 $$\int_\Omega \exp\left[\frac{|a_1 X_1 + \cdots + a_n X_n|^2}{16M^2(a_1^2 + \cdots + a_n^2)}\right] dP \leq \sqrt{2}.$$

We thus deduce the following remarkable

THEOREM 3.5.1. *Let $\{X_n\}$ be a sequence of independent uniformly bounded random variables, and let $|X_\nu| \leq M$. Suppose that the X_n's have mean zero and variance one so that they form an orthonormal set. Then any $f \in L_2$ which admits an expansion in terms of $\{X_n\}$, i.e., any f for which we have*

$$\lim_{n\to\infty} \int_\Omega \left| f - \sum_{\nu=1}^{n} a_\nu X_\nu \right|^2 dP = 0 \quad \left(\sum_{\nu=1}^{\infty} a_\nu^2 < \infty \right),$$

must necessarily be in every L_p class and furthermore

3.5.8 $$\int_\Omega e^{|f|^2/16M^2 \|f\|_2^2}\, dP \leq \sqrt{2}.$$

PROOF. This result is obtained simply by passing to the limit as $n \to \infty$ in 3.5.7 and using Fatou's lemma.

Remark. The constants in the inequality 3.5.3 cannot be improved. To show this we shall follow a very simple argument we owe to J. Holbrook.

Set $X_\nu = R_\nu$, where $R_1, R_2, \ldots, R_n$ are the Rademacher functions, and $a_1 = a_2 = \cdots = a_n = 1/\sqrt{n}$. We then have

$$\int_0^1 \left| \frac{R_1 + \cdots + R_n}{\sqrt{n}} \right|^{2p} dx = \frac{1}{n^p} \sum_{\left\{ \substack{\alpha_1 + \cdots + \alpha_n = 2p \\ \alpha_i = \text{even}} \right\}} \frac{(2p)!}{\alpha_1! \cdots \alpha_n!}$$

$$\geq \frac{1}{n^p} \sum_{\left\{ \substack{\alpha_1 + \cdots + \alpha_n = 2p \\ \alpha_i = 0 \text{ or } 2} \right\}} \frac{(2p)!}{\alpha_1! \cdots \alpha_n!}.$$

It is easy to see that when $\alpha_1 = 0$ or 2, $\alpha_1! \cdots \alpha_n! = 2^{(\alpha_1 + \cdots + \alpha_n)/2}$. Thus we obtain

$$\int_0^1 \left| \frac{R_1 + \cdots + R_n}{\sqrt{n}} \right|^{2p} dx \geq \frac{(2p)!}{2^p n^p} \frac{n(n-1) \cdots (n-p+1)}{p!}$$

$$= \frac{(2p)!}{2^p p!} \left(1 - \frac{1}{n}\right) \cdots \left(1 - \frac{p-1}{n}\right).$$

On the other hand, 3.5.3 would give in this case

$$\int_0^1 \left| \frac{R_1 + \cdots + R_n}{\sqrt{n}} \right|^{2p} dx \leq \frac{(2p)!}{2^p p!}.$$

3.6 SOME COMBINATORIAL INEQUALITIES

We have seen that some orthonormal systems $\{\Phi_n\}$ satisfy an inequality such as

3.6.1 $$\int_\Omega \max_{1 \leq \nu \leq n} (a_1 \Phi_1 + \cdots + a_\nu \Phi_\nu)^2 \, d\mu \leq C \sum_{\nu=1}^n a_\nu^2 \qquad \forall \; n \geq 1$$

with a constant C independent of n. We cannot, however, expect 3.6.1 to hold for arbitrary orthonormal systems, since such an inequality implies the a.e. convergence of the partial sums $S_n(x, f) = a_1 \Phi_1 + \cdots + a_n \Phi_n \; \forall f \in L_2$. Indeed, the best result obtained without additional assumptions on $\{\Phi_n\}$ is the inequality

3.6.2

$$\int_\Omega \max_{1 \leq \nu \leq n} (a_1 \Phi_1 + \cdots + a_\nu \Phi_\nu)^2 \, d\mu \leq 4(\log_2 n)^2 \sum_{\nu=1}^n a_\nu^2 \qquad (\forall \; n \geq 2).$$

This is a classical result of Menshov [31].

Menshov was also able to establish that the $(\log n)^2$ growth on the right-hand side of 3.6.2 is really necessary. For this reason this subject has been left dormant for many years.

Somewhat unexpectedly, however, it turns out that things are not as bad as all that and indeed in some sense 3.6.1 may very well be the rule rather than the exception. In fact, note that for a given orthonormal system the quantity

$$C_n(\Phi_1, \Phi_2, \ldots, \Phi_n) = \sup_{a^2 + \cdots + a^2 \leq 1} \int_\Omega \max_{1 \leq \nu \leq n} (a_1\Phi_1 + \cdots + a_\nu\Phi_\nu)^2 \, d\mu$$

must be seriously affected by a change in the order in which the functions $\Phi_1, \Phi_2, \ldots, \Phi_n$ are given. To see this it suffices to observe that for the Haar system we do have 3.6.1 (see 3.4.5) and yet by a suitable rearrangement even the a.e. convergence properties of the partial sums can be destroyed. We might thus suspect that although 3.6.2 is best possible for a system $\Phi_1, \Phi_2, \ldots, \Phi_n$ that is given in an arbitrary fashion, an inequality such as 3.6.1 with a universal C may yet be valid for an appropriate reordering $\Phi_{\sigma_1}, \Phi_{\sigma_2}, \ldots, \Phi_{\sigma_n}$ of $\Phi_1, \Phi_2, \ldots, \Phi_n$.

More precisely we can translate these thoughts in the following

Conjecture. *There is a universal constant C such that given any finite orthonormal system $\Phi_1, \Phi_2, \ldots, \Phi_n$ for some permutation $(\sigma_1, \sigma_2, \ldots, \sigma_n)$ of $(1, 2, \ldots, n)$ we have*

3.6.3 $$\sup_{a_1^2 + \cdots + a_n^2 \leq 1} \int_\Omega \max_{1 \leq \nu \leq n} (a_1\Phi_{\sigma_1} + \cdots + a_\nu\Phi_{\sigma_2})^2 \, d\mu \leq C.$$

This statement is perhaps too good to be true; nevertheless, we do have some evidence in its support; furthermore, our attempts at establishing it have led us to some rather interesting and useful combinatorial inequalities.

Before presenting this material we shall indicate briefly how this conjecture can be used to establish the existence of a.e. convergence-producing rearrangements.

A theorem of Marcinkiewicz [29] states that given any orthonormal system $\{\Phi_n\}$ it is possible to find an increasing sequence of integers $\{n_k\}$ such that the partial sums

$$S_{n_k}(x, f) = \sum_{\nu=1}^{n_k} a_\nu \Phi_\nu(x) \qquad \left(a_\nu = \int_\Omega f\Phi_\nu \, d\mu\right)$$

converge a.e. $\forall f \in L_2$. In addition, if we set

$$\mathcal{O}^*(x, f) = \sup_{k \geq 1} |S_{n_k}(x, f)|,$$

then for some constant C we have

$$\text{3.6.4} \qquad \int_\Omega [\mathcal{O}^*(x, f)]^2 \, d\mu \leq C \int_\Omega |f|^2 \, d\mu.$$

In the search for an a.e. convergence-producing rearrangement $\Phi_{\sigma_1}, \Phi_{\sigma_2}, \ldots, \Phi_{\sigma_n}, \ldots$ of the system $\Phi_1, \Phi_2, \ldots, \Phi_n, \ldots$ the theorem of Marcinkiewicz suggests that we look for rearrangements of a special type, namely those corresponding to permutations $(\sigma_1, \sigma_2, \ldots, \sigma_n, \ldots)$ of the integers which interchange the elements of each of the blocks

$$n_k + 1, n_k + 2, \ldots, n_k + m_k \qquad (m_k = n_{k+1} - n_k)$$

only among themselves. Of course, then the resulting rearranged system $\{\Phi_{\sigma_n}\}$ will have the same partial sums of order n_k as the old one. The hope is that we can find a $\{\sigma_n\}$ of this type which improves the behavior of partial sums with in-between indices.

It is clear what role the inequality 3.6.3 would play in this program. Indeed, if the conjecture is true, it is then possible to find a block-type permutation $\{\sigma_n\}$ such that for each k,

$$\sup_{a_1^2 + \cdots + a_{m_k}^2 \leq 1} \int_\Omega \max_{1 \leq \nu \leq m_k} (a_1 \Phi_{\sigma_{n_k+1}} + a_2 \Phi_{\sigma_{n_k+2}} + \cdots + a_{m_k} \Phi_{\sigma_{n_k+m_k}})^2 \, d\mu \leq C.$$

In other words, if we set

$$S_n(x, \sigma, f) = \sum_{\nu=1}^{n} a_{\sigma_\nu} \Phi_{\sigma_\nu} \qquad \left(a_n = \int_\Omega f \Phi_n \, d\mu\right)$$

for the partial sum of the expansion of a given $f \in L_2$ in terms of the rearranged system, we shall necessarily have

$$\int_\Omega \max_{n_k < n \leq n_{k+1}} (S_n(x, \sigma, f) - S_{n_k}(x, \sigma, f))^2 \, d\mu \leq C \sum_{n=n_k+1}^{n_{k+1}} a_n^2.$$

Summing these inequalities we would obtain

$$\text{3.6.5} \qquad \int_\Omega \left\{ \sum_{k=1}^{\infty} \max_{n_k < n \leq n_{k+1}} [S_n - S_{n_k}]^2 \right\} d\mu \leq C \int_\Omega |f|^2 \, d\mu < \infty.$$

This would imply the almost everywhere convergence of the partial sums $S_n(x, \sigma, f)$. Indeed, from 3.6.5 we not only get

$$\max_{n_k < n \leq n_{k+1}} |S_n(x, \sigma, f) - S_{n_k}(x, \sigma, f)| \to 0 \quad \text{a.e.} \qquad \forall \;\; f \in L_2,$$

but in combination with 3.6.4 we would obtain also an inequality of type 3.6.1 for the rearranged system $\{\Phi_{\sigma_n}\}$.

A first test of the validity of the conjecture comes from the following observations. There are systems $\Phi_1, \Phi_2, \dots, \Phi_n$, which are essentially left unchanged by any permutation. If the conjecture is true, then for such systems we must have 3.6.1 to begin with.

We can make this remark more explicit. The simplest but rather exhaustive class of finite orthonormal systems on a probability space can be obtained as follows. We take $\Omega = E_n = n$-dimensional Euclidean space, $\mathscr{F} = \mathscr{B} = \{\text{Borel sets}\}$ and P the probability measure on E_n,

$$P(E) = \int_E f(x_1, x_2, \dots, x_n)\, dx_1 \cdots dx_n$$

induced by a Borel-measurable function $f(x_1, x_2, \dots, x_n)$ satisfying the conditions

(a) $f(x_1, x_2, \dots, x_n) \geq 0$;

(b) $\displaystyle\int_{-\infty}^{+\infty} \cdots \int_{-\infty}^{+\infty} f(x_1, x_2, \dots, x_n)\, dx_1 \cdots dx_n = 1.$

We then set

$$\Phi_1(x_1, x_2, \dots, x_n) = x_1, \Phi_2(x_1, x_2, \dots, x_n) = x_2, \dots$$
$$\Phi_n(x_1, x_2, \dots, x_n) = x_n.$$

The system $\Phi_1, \Phi_2, \dots, \Phi_n$ will be orthonormal if and only if $f(x_1, x_2, \cdots, x_n)$ in addition to (a) and (b) satisfies

(c) $\displaystyle\int_{-\infty}^{+\infty} \cdots \int_{-\infty}^{+\infty} x_i x_j f(x_1, x_2, \dots, x_n)\, dx_1 \cdots dx_n = \delta_{ij}.$

Our conjecture is thus concerned with the quantity

$$Q(\sigma, f) = \sup_{a_1^2 + \cdots + a_n^2 \leq 1} \int_{-\infty}^{+\infty} \cdots \int_{-\infty}^{+\infty} \max_{1 \leq \nu \leq n} (a_1 \chi_{\sigma_1} + \cdots + a_\nu \chi_{\sigma_\nu})^2$$
$$\times f(x_1, \dots, x_n)\, dx_1 \cdots dx_n$$

as f is restricted to satisfy the conditions (a), (b), and (c).

Note that by a change of variables we can write

$$Q(\sigma, f) = \sup_{a_1^2 + \cdots + a_n^2 \leq 1} \int_{-\infty}^{+\infty} \cdots \int_{-\infty}^{+\infty} \max_{1 \leq \nu \leq n} (a_1 x_1 + \cdots + a_\nu x_\nu)^2$$

$$\times f(x_{\pi 1}, x_{\pi 2}, \ldots, x_{\pi n})\, dx_1 \cdots dx_n,$$

where $(\pi_1, \pi_2, \ldots, \pi_n)$ denotes the permutation inverse of $(\sigma_1, \sigma_2, \ldots, \sigma_n)$. If $f(x_1, x_2, \ldots, x_n)$ happens to be a symmetric function; in other words, if f satisfies the condition

$$\text{(d)}.\ f(x_{\sigma_1}, x_{\sigma_2}, \ldots, x_{\sigma_n}) = f(x_1, x_2, \ldots, x_n) \qquad \forall \quad \sigma = (\sigma_1, \sigma_2, \ldots, \sigma_n),$$

the quantity $Q(\sigma, f)$ is independent of σ and then permuting Φ_1, $\Phi_2, \ldots, \Phi_n$ cannot possibly do any good. So if the conjecture is true, we must have the inequality

3.6.6
$$\int_{-\infty}^{+\infty} \cdots \int_{-\infty}^{+\infty} \max_{1 \leq \nu \leq n} (a_1 x_1 + \cdots + a_\nu x_\nu)^2 f(x_1, x_2, \ldots, x_n)$$

$$\times\, dx_1 \cdots dx_n \leq C \sum_{\nu=1}^{n} a_\nu^2$$

for all reals $(a_1, a_2, \ldots, a_n)$ and for all functions $f(x_1, x_2, \ldots, x_n)$ satisfying the condition (a), (b), (c), and (d).

Now, if we start with an arbitrary function satisfying (a), (b), and (c) the symmetrized function

$$\frac{1}{n!} \sum_{\sigma} f(x_{\sigma_1}, x_{\sigma_2}, \ldots, x_{\sigma_n})$$

also satisfies (d). Thus substituting this function for f in 3.6.6 we deduce that

If the conjecture is true, for some universal constant C we must have

$$\frac{1}{n!} \sum_{\sigma} \int_{-\infty}^{+\infty} \cdots \int_{-\infty}^{+\infty} \max_{1 \leq \nu \leq n} (a_1 x_1 + \cdots + a_\nu x_\nu)^2 f(x_{\sigma_1}, x_{\sigma_2}, \ldots, x_{\sigma_n})$$

$$\times\, dx_1 \cdots dx_n \leq C \sum_{\nu=1}^{n} a_\nu^2.$$

Or, equivalently (by a change of variables), we must have

3.6.7
$$\frac{1}{n!}\sum_{\sigma}\int_{-\infty}^{+\infty}\cdots\int_{-\infty}^{+\infty}\max_{1\leq\nu\leq n}(a_1x_{\sigma_1}+\cdots+a_\nu x_{\sigma_\nu})^2 \times f(x_1,x_2,\ldots,x_n)\,dx_1\cdots dx_n \leq C\sum_{\nu=1}^{n}a_\nu^2$$

for all functions f satisfying (a), (b), and (c) all reals $(a_1, a_2, \ldots, a_n)$.

One might guess that if for some function $g \geq 0$ we have an inequality such as

3.6.8
$$\int_{-\infty}^{+\infty}\cdots\int_{-\infty}^{+\infty} g(x_1,x_2,\ldots,x_n)f(x_1,x_2,\ldots,x_n)\,dx_1\cdots dx_n \leq C,$$

for all f satisfying (a), (b), and (c), then g must satisfy some pointwise inequality. On the other hand, it is easily seen that any function of the type

$$\sum_{i\neq j=1}^{n} A_{ij}x_ix_j + \sum_{i=1}^{n} B_i(x_i^2 - 1) + C$$

does satisfy 3.6.8 for all such f. Thus the best we can hope to deduce from 3.6.8 is

3.6.9
$$g \leq \sum_{i\neq j=1}^{n} A_{ij}x_ix_j + \sum_{i=1}^{n} B_i(x_i^2 - 1) + C$$

for some real constants A_{ij} and B_i.

And indeed it was shown by Holbrook [17] that the validity of 3.6.8 for all f satisfying (a), (b), and (c) does imply 3.6.9.

Applying this result to

$$g = \frac{1}{n!}\sum_{\sigma}\max_{1\leq\nu\leq n}(a_1x_{\sigma_1}+\cdots+a_\nu x_{\sigma_\nu})^2$$

and using the symmetry of this function, from 3.6.9 we can easily deduce that there are constants A, B such that for all $x_1, x_2, \ldots, x_n$,

3.6.10
$$\frac{1}{n!}\sum_{\sigma}\max_{1\leq\nu\leq n}(a_1x_{\sigma_1}+\cdots+a_\nu x_{\sigma_\nu})^2 \leq A\left[\left(\sum_{i=1}^{n}x_i\right)^2 - n\right] + B\left[\sum_{i=1}^{n}x_i^2 - n\right] + C,$$

at least when $a_1, a_2,\dots, a_n$ are kept fixed and

$$a_1^2 + a_2^2 + \cdots + a_n^2 = 1.$$

By setting $x_1 = x_2 = \cdots = x_n = 1/\sqrt{n}$ we obtain

3.6.11 $$B \leq \frac{C}{n-1},$$

while setting $x_1 = \sqrt{n/2}$, $x_2 = -\sqrt{n/2}$, $x_3 = \cdots = x_n = 0$ gives

3.6.12 $$A \leq \frac{C}{n}.$$

Finally, replacing $x_1, x_2,\dots, x_n$ in 3.6.10 by $tx_1, tx_2,\dots, tx_n$ dividing by t and letting $t \to \infty$ we deduce

$$\frac{1}{n!}\sum_{\sigma} \max_{1 \leq \nu \leq n} [a_1 x_{\sigma_1} + \cdots + a_\nu x_{\sigma_\nu}]^2 \leq A\left(\sum_{\nu=1}^{n} x_\nu\right)^2 + B\left(\sum_{\nu=1}^{n} x_\nu^2\right).$$

Combining this inequality with 3.6.11 and 3.6.12 we must conclude that

If the conjecture is true, for some universal constant C, we must have

3.6.13 $$\frac{1}{n!}\sum_{\sigma} \max_{1 \leq \nu \leq n} [a_1 x_{\sigma_1} + \cdots + a_\nu x_{\sigma_\nu}]^2 \leq \frac{C}{n}\left(\sum_{\nu=1}^{n} x_\nu\right)^2 + \frac{C}{n-1}\left(\sum_{\nu=1}^{n} x_\nu^2\right),$$

for all reals $(a_1, a_2,\dots, a_n)$ normalized by

$$a_1^2 + a_2^2 + \cdots + a_n^2 = 1.$$

Remark 3.6.1. Suppose, on the other hand, that 3.6.13 does hold. Let $\Phi_1(x), \Phi_2(x),\dots, \Phi_n(x)$ be an orthonormal system on some finite or infinite measure space $(\Omega, \mathscr{F}, \mu)$; then substituting $\Phi_1(x), \Phi_2(x),\dots, \Phi_n(x)$ for $x_1, x_2,\dots, x_n$ in 3.6.13 and integrating over Ω we obtain

3.6.14 $$\frac{1}{n!}\sum_{\sigma} \int_{\Omega} \max_{1 \leq \nu \leq n} (a_1 \Phi_{\sigma_1} + \cdots + a_\nu \Phi_{\sigma_\nu})^2 \, d\mu \leq 3C \sum_{\nu=1}^{n} a_\nu^2,$$

for all $n > 1$ and all $a_1, a_2,\dots, a_n$.

When the functions $\Phi_1, \Phi_2, \dots, \Phi_n$ are "*interchangeable*," i.e., when for all permutations $\sigma = (\sigma_1, \sigma_2, \dots, \sigma_n)$ for all reals $\alpha_1, \alpha_2, \dots, \alpha_n$ we have

$$\mu\{\Phi_{\sigma_1} \leq \alpha_1, \dots, \Phi_{\sigma_n} \leq \alpha_n\} = \mu\{\Phi_1 \leq \alpha_1, \dots, \Phi_n \leq \alpha_n\},$$

then for all σ,

$$\int_\Omega \max_{1 \leq \nu \leq n} (a_1 \Phi_{\sigma_1} + \cdots + a_\nu \Phi_{\sigma_\nu})^2 \, d\mu$$

$$= \int_\Omega \max_{1 \leq \nu \leq n} (a_1 \Phi_1 + \cdots + a_\nu \Phi_\nu)^2 \, d\mu$$

and thus in this case 3.6.14 yields

$$\int_\Omega \max_{1 \leq \nu \leq n} (a_1 \Phi_1 + \cdots + a_\nu \Phi_\nu)^2 \, d\mu \leq 3C \sum_{\nu=1}^{n} a_\nu^2.$$

Remark 3.6.2. If we set $a_1 = a_2 = \cdots = a_n = 1/\sqrt{n}$ in 3.6.13 we deduce

3.6.15 $$\frac{1}{n!} \sum_\sigma \max_{1 \leq \nu \leq n} (x_{\sigma_1} + \cdots + x_{\sigma_\nu})^2 \leq C \left(\sum_{\nu=1}^{n} x_\nu \right)^2 + 2C \left(\sum_{\nu=1}^{n} x_\nu^2 \right)$$

for $n > 1$. Replacing $x_1, x_2, \dots, x_n$ by $a_1 \Phi_1(x), \dots, a_n \Phi_n(x)$, respectively, and integrating we get

3.6.16 $$\frac{1}{n!} \sum_\sigma \int_\Omega \max_{1 \leq \nu \leq n} (a_{\sigma_1} \Phi_{\sigma_1} + \cdots + a_{\sigma_\nu} \Phi_{\sigma_\nu})^2 \, d\mu \leq 3C \sum_{\nu=1}^{n} a_\nu^2.$$

This inequality implies that given any constants $a_1, a_2, \dots, a_n$ and any orthonormal system $\Phi_1, \Phi_2, \dots, \Phi_n$ there is at least one permutation $(\sigma_1, \sigma_2, \dots, \sigma_n)$ such that

$$\int_\Omega \max_{1 \leq \nu \leq n} (a_{\sigma_1} \Phi_{\sigma_1} + \cdots + a_{\sigma_\nu} \Phi_{\sigma_\nu})^2 \, d\mu \leq 3C \sum_{\nu=1}^{n} a_\nu^2.$$

In 1962 we indeed established 3.6.16 (with $3C = 16$), and this result permitted us to prove that any orthonormal expansion

$$a_1 \Phi_1(x) + \cdots + a_n \Phi_n(x) + \cdots$$

admits an almost everywhere convergent rearrangement.

In the next section we shall prove that 3.6.13 is indeed true, and we shall thus obtain a proof that the conjecture is true at least for orthonormal systems of interchangeable functions.

3.7 A PROOF OF THE COMBINATORIAL INEQUALITIES

In this section we shall present a proof of the inequality 3.6.13 and the same time obtain a whole class of similar inequalities.

The basic step here will be to write the left-hand side of the inequality 3.6.13 in a form which allows it to be studied by the classical Kolmogorov methods, i.e., the methods of Section 3.2. To this end we introduce a probability space Ω whose points are the $n!$ permutations

$$\sigma = (\sigma_1, \sigma_2, \dots, \sigma_n)$$

of the integers $(1, 2, \dots, n)$. To each permutation σ we assign probability $P(\sigma) = 1/n!$.

Given n reals $x_1, x_2, \dots, x_n$ we introduce the functions $\Phi_1(\sigma)$, $\Phi_2(\sigma), \dots, \Phi_n(\sigma)$ by setting, when $\sigma = (\sigma_1, \sigma_2, \dots, \sigma_n)$,

$$\Phi_1(\sigma) = x_{\sigma_1}, \Phi_2(\sigma) = x_{\sigma_2}, \dots, \Phi_n(\sigma) = x_{\sigma_n}.$$

Also, for a set of coefficients $a = (a_1, a_2, \dots, a_n)$ we introduce the partial sums

$$S_\nu(\sigma) = S_\nu(\sigma, a) = a_1\Phi_1(\sigma) + \cdots + a_\nu\Phi_\nu(\sigma)$$

and their majorants

$$S_\nu^*(\sigma) = S_\nu^*(\sigma, a) = \max_{1 \le \mu \le \nu} |S_\mu(\sigma)|.$$

With this notation the left-hand side of 3.6.13 can be written in the form

$$\int_\Omega [S_n^*(\sigma, a)]^2 \, dP.$$

This suggests we may try as we have done many times before to establish some sort of estimate for $S_n^*(\sigma, a)$ of the type given by Proposition 3.2.1.

Before we proceed in this manner, it is convenient to introduce the functions

$$\mathcal{O}_\nu(\sigma) = \Phi_1(\sigma) + \cdots + \Phi_\nu(\sigma), \qquad \mathcal{O}_\nu^*(\sigma) = \max_{1 \le \mu \le \nu} |\mathcal{O}_\mu(\sigma)|.$$

Also, for technical reasons, we shall have to work first with $S_m^*(\sigma, a)$, where

3.7.1 $$m = \frac{n+1}{2},$$

and we shall assume, unless otherwise explicitly stated, that

$$x_1 + x_2 + \cdots + x_n = 0. \tag{3.7.2}$$

In trying to follow the methods used in the proof of Proposition 3.2.1 we quickly run into difficulties since the functions $S_\nu(\sigma)$ do not satisfy the martingale equalities

$$\int_E S_m \, dP = \int_E S_\nu \, dP \qquad \forall \quad E \in \mathscr{F}(S_1, S_2, \ldots, S_\nu), \quad \forall \quad \nu \leq m,$$

nor even the corresponding martingale inequalities. This we are led to calculate the integrals

$$\int_E (S_m - S_\nu) \, dP = \sum_{l=\nu+1}^{m} a_l \int_E \Phi_l \, dP \qquad \forall \quad E \in \mathscr{F}(S_1, S_2, \ldots, S_\nu).$$

This is easily done by means of the following

LEMMA 3.7.1. *If $E \in \mathscr{F}(\Phi_1, \Phi_2, \ldots, \Phi_\nu)$, then for any $\nu + 1 \leq l \leq n$*

$$\int_E \Phi_l \, dP = \frac{1}{n-\nu} \int_E (\Phi_{\nu+1} + \cdots + \Phi_n) \, dP \tag{3.7.3}$$

$$= -\frac{1}{n-\nu} \int_E \mathscr{O}_\nu(\sigma) \, dP.$$

PROOF. To such a subset E of Ω we can associate a collection $\mathscr{E}$ of ν-tuples $(i_1, i_2, \ldots, i_\nu)$ of distinct integers between 1 and n by the requirement that

$$(i_1, i_2, \ldots, i_\nu) \in \mathscr{E} \Leftrightarrow \{\sigma : \sigma_1 = i_1, \ldots, \sigma_\nu = i_\nu\} \subset E.$$

Whether or not a given $\sigma = (\sigma_1, \ldots, \sigma_n)$ belongs to E only depends upon its first ν entries $(\sigma_1, \sigma_2, \ldots, \sigma_\nu)$ we can thus decompose E into the disjoint union

$$E = \sum_{(i_1, i_2, \ldots, i_\nu) \in \mathscr{E}} \{\sigma : \sigma_1 = i_1, \ldots, \sigma_\nu = i_\nu\}. \tag{3.7.4}$$

This given, we can write

$$\int_E \Phi_l \, dP = \sum_{(i_1, i_2, \ldots, i_\nu) \in \mathscr{E}} \int_{\{\sigma : \sigma_1 = i_1, \ldots, \sigma_\nu = i_\nu\}} \Phi_l \, dP. \tag{3.7.5}$$

On the other hand, it is clear that for every $(i_1, i_2, \ldots, i_\nu) \in \mathscr{E}$ we have

3.7.6 $$\int_{\{\sigma:\sigma_1=i_1,\ldots,\sigma_\nu=i_\nu\}} \Phi_l \, dP = \sum_{k\notin(i_1,\ldots,i_\nu)} x_k P\{\sigma : \sigma_1 = i_1, \ldots, \sigma_\nu = i_\nu \,;\, \sigma_{\nu+1} = k\}.$$

Trivially,

$$P\{\sigma : \sigma_1 = i_1, \ldots, \sigma_\nu = i_\nu ; \sigma_{\nu+1} = k\} = \frac{(n-\nu-1)!}{n!}.$$

Substituting in 3.7.6 and using 3.7.2

$$\int_{\{\sigma:\sigma_1=i_1,\ldots,\sigma_\nu=i_\nu\}} \Phi_l \, dP = \frac{(n-\nu-1)!}{n!} \sum_{k\notin(i_1,\ldots,i_\nu)} x_k$$
$$= -\frac{(x_{i_1} + \cdots + x_{i_\nu})}{n-\nu} \frac{(n-\nu)!}{n!}$$
$$= \frac{-1}{n-\nu} \int_{\{\sigma:\sigma_1=i_1,\ldots,\sigma_\nu=i_\nu\}} \mathscr{O}_\nu(\sigma) \, dP.$$

Cómbining with 3.7.5, 3.7.3 follows immediately.†

The crucial step is the following

LEMMA 3.7.2. *Let* $E = \sum_{\nu=1}^{m} E_\nu$, *where for each* ν $E_\nu \in \mathscr{F}(\Phi_1, \Phi_2, \ldots, \Phi_\nu)$, *then*

3.7.7 $$\sum_{\nu=1}^{m} \int_{E_\nu} |S_\nu| \, dP \le \int_E |S_m| \, dP + \sum_{\nu=1}^{m} \frac{|a_{\nu+1} + \cdots + a_m|}{n-\nu} \int_{E_\nu} |\mathscr{O}_\nu| \, dP.$$

PROOF. Define

$$E_\nu^+ = E_\nu \cap \{S_\nu \ge 0\}, \qquad E_\nu^- = E_\nu \cap \{S_\nu < 0\};$$

then write

3.7.8 $$\int_{E_\nu} |S_\nu| \, dP = \int_{E_\nu^+} S_\nu \, dP - \int_{E_\nu^-} S_\nu \, dP.$$

† The assertion of the lemma follows immediately if we use the fact, well known among statisticians, that the variables $x_{\sigma_{\nu+1}}, \ldots, x_{\sigma_n}$ are identically distributed once $x_{\sigma_1}, \ldots, x_{\sigma_\nu}$ are given.

Since $E_\nu^+ \in \mathscr{F}(\Phi_1, \Phi_2, \ldots, \Phi_\nu)$, by Lemma 3.7.1 we get

$$\int_{E_\nu^+} S_\nu \, dP = \int_{E_\nu^+} S_m \, dP - \int_{E_\nu^+} (S_m - S_\nu) \, dP$$

$$= \int_{E_\nu^+} S_m \, dP + \frac{a_{\nu+1} + \cdots + a_m}{n - \nu} \int_{E_\nu^+} \mathcal{O}_\nu \, dP.$$

Thus

$$\int_{E_\nu^+} |S_\nu| \, dP \leq \int_{E_\nu^+} |S_m| \, dP + \frac{|a_{\nu+1} + \cdots + a_m|}{n - \nu} \int_{E_\nu^+} |\mathcal{O}_\nu| \, dP.$$

Similarly, we get

$$-\int_{E_\nu^-} S_\nu \, dP \leq \int_{E_\nu^-} |S_m| \, dP + \frac{|a_{\nu+1} + \cdots + a_m|}{n - \nu} \int_{E_\nu^-} |\mathcal{O}_\nu| \, dP.$$

Combining these two inequalities with 3.7.8 and summing for $\nu = 1, 2, \ldots, m$, 3.7.7 follows immediately.

We are now finally in a position to state and prove our basic inequalities.

PROPOSITION 3.7.1. *For any $\lambda > 0$ we have*

3.7.9
$$P\{\mathcal{O}_m^* > \lambda\} \leq \frac{2}{\lambda} \int_{\{\mathcal{O}_m^* > \lambda\}} |\mathcal{O}_m| \, dP.$$

PROOF. Setting $a_1 = a_2 = \cdots = a_n = 1$ in 3.7.7 we get

$$\sum_{\nu=1}^{m} \int_{E_\nu} |\mathcal{O}_\nu| \, dP \leq \int_E |\mathcal{O}_m| \, dP + \sum_{\nu=1}^{m} \frac{m - \nu}{n - \nu} \int_{E_\nu} |\mathcal{O}_\nu| \, dP,$$

or, better yet,

3.7.10
$$\sum_{\nu=1}^{m} \frac{n - m}{n - \nu} \int_{E_\nu} |\mathcal{O}_\nu| \, dP \leq \int_E |\mathcal{O}_m| \, dP,$$

and this holds provided $E = \sum_{\nu=1}^{m} E_\nu$† with $E_\nu \in \mathscr{F}(\Phi_1, \Phi_2, \ldots, \Phi_\nu)$. From the definition of m (3.7.1) we get

$$\frac{n - m}{n - \nu} \geq \frac{1}{2} \qquad \text{for } \nu = 1, 2, \ldots, m.$$

† The symbol $\sum$ stands for *disjoint union.*

Thus 3.7.9 follows immediately from 3.7.10 upon setting

$$E_\nu = \{|\mathcal{O}_1| \le \lambda,\ldots, |\mathcal{O}_{\nu-1}| \le \lambda ; |\mathcal{O}_\nu| > \lambda\},$$

$$E = \sum_{\nu=1}^{m} E_\nu .$$

PROPOSITION 3.7.2. *For any $\lambda > 0$, and any reals $a_1, a_2,\ldots, a_n$ such that*

3.7.11 $$a_1^2 + a_2^2 + \cdots + a_n^2 \le 1,$$

we have

3.7.12 $$P\{S_m^* > \lambda\} \le \frac{1}{\lambda}\int_{\{S_m^* > \lambda\}} |S_m|\, dP + \frac{\sqrt{2}}{\lambda\sqrt{n-1}}\int_{\{S_m^* > \lambda\}} |\mathcal{O}_m|\, dP.$$

PROOF. We set here

$$E_\nu = \{|S_1| \le \lambda,\ldots, |S_{\nu-1}| \le \lambda ; \qquad |S_\nu| > \lambda\},\ E = \sum_{\nu=1}^{m} E_\nu .$$

By Lemma 3.7.2 and Schwarz's inequality (together with 3.7.11) we get

3.7.13 $$\sum_{\nu=1}^{m} \int_{E_\nu} |S_\nu|\, dP \le \int_E |S_m|\, dP + \sum_{\nu=1}^{m} \frac{\sqrt{m-\nu}}{n-\nu}\int_{E_\nu} |\mathcal{O}_\nu|\, dP.$$

Note that since $E_\nu \in \mathscr{F}(\Phi_1, \Phi_2,\ldots, \Phi_\nu)$ the inequality 3.7.10 again holds; thus we get

$$\sum_{\nu=1}^{m} \frac{\sqrt{m-\nu}}{n-\nu}\int_{E_\nu} |\mathcal{O}_\nu|\, dP \le \frac{\sqrt{2}}{\sqrt{n-1}} \sum_{\nu=1}^{m} \frac{n-m}{n-\nu}\int_{E_\nu} |\mathcal{O}_\nu|\, dP$$

$$\le \frac{\sqrt{2}}{\sqrt{n-1}}\int_E |\mathcal{O}_m|\, dP.$$

Combining with 3.7.13 we get 3.7.12 upon replacing in each E_ν $|S_\nu|$ by λ. As a corollary to Proposition 3.7.2, we obtain our inequality 3.6.13. In other words,

THEOREM 3.7.1. *If $a_1, a_2,\ldots, a_n$ are such that*

3.7.14 $$a_1^2 + \cdots + a_n^2 \le 1,$$

then for all reals $(x_1, x_2, \dots, x_n)$ *we have*

3.7.15
$$\frac{1}{n!}\sum_{\sigma} \max_{1 \le \nu \le n} (a_1 x_{\sigma 1} + \cdots + a_\nu x_{\sigma_\nu})^2 \le \frac{81}{n}\left(\sum_{\nu=1}^{n} x_\nu\right)^2 + \frac{81}{n-1}\left(\sum_{\nu=1}^{n} x_\nu^2\right).$$

PROOF. Multiplying (as in the proof of the strong estimate theorem 2.2.3) the inequality 3.7.12 by λ and integrating $d\lambda$ from 0 to ∞ we get

$$\tfrac{1}{2}\int_\Omega [S_m^*]^2\, dP \le \int_\Omega |S_m| S_m^*\, dP + \frac{\sqrt{2}}{\sqrt{n-1}}\int_\Omega |\mathcal{O}_m| S_m^*\, dP.$$

By Schwartz's inequality,

3.7.16
$$\tfrac{1}{2}\left[\int_\Omega [S_m^*]^2\, dP\right]^{1/2} \le \left(\int_\Omega |S_m|^2\, dP\right)^{1/2} + \frac{\sqrt{2}}{\sqrt{n-1}}\left(\int_\Omega |\mathcal{O}_m|^2\, dP\right)^{1/2}.$$

Going back to our definitions

$$\int_\Omega S_m^2\, dP = \frac{1}{n!}\sum_\sigma (a_1 x_{\sigma 1} + \cdots + a_m x_{\sigma m})^2 = \sum_{\nu=1}^{m} a_\nu^2 \frac{1}{n!}\sum_\sigma x_{\sigma_\nu}^2 + \sum_{\nu \ne \mu = 1}^{n} a_\nu a_\mu \frac{1}{n!}\sum_\sigma x_{\sigma_\nu} x_{\sigma_\mu}.$$

It is easily seen that

$$\frac{1}{n!}\sum_\sigma x_{\sigma_\nu}^2 = \frac{1}{n}\sum_{\alpha=1}^{n} x_\alpha^2, \qquad \frac{1}{n!}\sum_\sigma x_{\sigma_\nu} x_{\sigma_\mu} = \frac{1}{n(n-1)}\sum_{\alpha \ne \beta = 1}^{n} x_\alpha x_\beta.$$

And so we can write, using the assumption $x_1 + x_2 + \cdots + x_n = 0$,

3.7.17
$$\int_\Omega |S_m|^2\, dP = \frac{1}{n}\left(\sum_{\nu=1}^{m} a_\nu^2\right)\left(\sum_{\alpha=1}^{n} x_\alpha^2\right) - \frac{1}{n(n-1)}\left(\sum_{\nu \ne \mu = 1}^{m} a_\nu a_\mu\right)\left(\sum_{\alpha=1}^{n} x_\alpha^2\right);$$

then, using 3.7.14,

3.7.18 $$\int_\Omega |S_m|^2\,dP \le \frac{3/2}{n-1}\left(\sum_{\alpha=1}^{n} x_\alpha^2\right).†$$

In a similar way we get also

$$\int_\Omega |\mathcal{O}_m|^2\,dP = \frac{m}{n}\,\frac{n-m}{n}\sum_{\nu=1}^{n} x_\nu^2 \le \tfrac{1}{2}\sum_{\nu=1}^{n} x_\nu^2.$$

Combining 3.7.17 and 3.7.18 with 3.7.16,

3.7.19 $$\frac{1}{n!}\sum_\sigma \max_{1\le\nu\le m}\,(a_1x_{\sigma_1} + \cdots + a_\nu x_{\sigma_\nu})^2$$

$$= \int_\Omega [S_m^*]^2\,dP \le \frac{20}{n-1}\sum_{\nu=1}^{n} x_\nu^2.$$

To get an estimate for S_n^* we observe that for $m < \nu \le n$,

$$S_\nu(\sigma, a) = S_\nu(\sigma, a) - S_m(\sigma, a) + S_m(\sigma, a) = S_{\nu-m}(\sigma', b) + S_m(\sigma, a),$$

where $b = (b_1,\dots, b_n)$ is any vector such that $b_\nu = a_{m+\nu}$, $\nu = 1, 2,\dots, n-m$ and σ' is obtained by the circular permutation from σ which is such that $\sigma'_\nu = \sigma_{m+\nu}$ ($\nu = 1, 2,\dots, n-m$). We thus have

$$S_n^*(\sigma, a) \le S_m^*(\sigma', b) + S_m^*(\sigma, a).$$

By Minkowsky's inequality we obtain

$$\left[\int_\Omega [S_n^*(\sigma, a)]^2\,dP\right]^{1/2}$$

$$\le \left(\int_\Omega [S_m^*(\sigma', b)]^2\,dP\right)^{1/2} + \left(\int_\Omega [S_m(\sigma, a)]^2\,dP\right)^{1/2};$$

3.7.19 then gives

3.7.20 $$\int_\Omega [S_n^*]^2\,dP \le \frac{80}{n-1}\sum_{\nu=1}^{n} x_\nu^2.$$

We finally need to eliminate the condition $x_1 + x_2 + \cdots + x_n = 0$. To do this we apply 3.7.20 to the variables $y_\nu = x_\nu - T$ with

† We can write

$$\sum_{\nu\ne\mu=1}^{m} a_\nu a_\mu = \left(\sum_{\nu=1}^{m} a_\nu\right)^2 - \sum_{\nu=1}^{n} a_\nu^2.$$

$T = (1/n)\sum_{\nu=1}^{n} x_\nu$ and use the relation

$$S_n^*(\sigma, a) \le \max_{1 \le \nu \le n} |a_1 y_{\sigma_1} + \cdots + a_\nu y_{\sigma_\nu}| + \sqrt{n}\,|T|,$$

to obtain

$$\left[\int_\Omega [S_n^*(\sigma, a)]^2\, dP\right]^{1/2} \le \left[\frac{80}{n-1}\sum_{\nu=1}^{n} y_\nu^2\right]^{1/2} + \sqrt{n}\,|T|,$$

and this inequality implies 3.7.15.

3.8 HISTORICAL REMARKS AND FURTHER INEQUALITIES

Our original [13] method of establishing such combinatorial inequalities was based upon a remarkable combinatorial lemma of Spitzer [38]. This lemma can be stated as follows.

Let $x_1, x_2, \ldots, x_n$ be real numbers and set for each permutation $\sigma = (\sigma_1, \sigma_2, \ldots, \sigma_n)$

$$S_n^*(\sigma) = \max_{1 \le \nu \le n} (x_{\sigma_1} + x_{\sigma_2} + \cdots + x_{\sigma_\nu})^+.$$

Furthermore, let $\chi(\sigma, \gamma)$ be defined for each permutation σ and each cycle γ to be 1 or 0 according as γ does or does not appear in the factorization of σ into a product of maximal cycles. Set

$$L_n^+(\sigma) = \sum_\gamma \chi(\sigma, \gamma)\Big(\sum_{i \in \gamma} x_i\Big)^+ .\dagger$$

Spitzer's lemma states that for any function $F(x)$ we have

$$\sum_\sigma F(S_n^+(\sigma)) = \sum_\sigma F(L_n^+(\sigma)).$$

In other words, the lists of numbers obtained from $S_n^+(\sigma)$ and $L_n^+(\sigma)$ by letting σ describe all $n!$ permutations are exactly the same.

Using this fact it can be shown, by following the same steps as in the proof of theorem 1.2 of [13], that

3.8.1 $$\frac{1}{n!}\sum_\sigma \max_{1 \le \nu \le n} (x_{\sigma_1} + \cdots + x_{\sigma_\nu})^2 \le 16\left(\sum_{\nu=1}^{n} x_\nu\right)^2 + 16\left(\sum_{\nu=1}^{n} x_\nu^2\right).$$

† Here we use the same symbol γ to represent a given cycle and the set consisting of those among the integers $(1, 2, \ldots, n)$ which appear in it.

After we were led to the inequality

3.8.2
$$\frac{1}{n!}\sum_{\sigma} \max_{1 \le v \le n} (a_1 x_{\sigma_1} + \cdots + a_v x_{\sigma_v})^2 \le \frac{C}{n}\left(\sum_{v=1}^{n} x_v\right)^2 + \frac{C}{n-1}\left(\sum_{v=1}^{n} x_v^2\right)$$

(via the conjecture of Section 3.6), our first attempts at establishing it were in the direction of seeking for a combinatorial identity of Spitzer's type concerning the quantities

$$S_n^+(\sigma) = \max_{1 \le v \le n} (a_1 x_{\sigma_1} + \cdots + a_v x_{\sigma_v})^+.$$

This approach leads to very interesting but unfortunately very difficult questions which still remain unsettled.

Later in the spring of 1966 L. Carleson, after being exposed to our inequality 3.8.1, pointed out to us that Rosén had also been concerned with expressions of the type

$$\max_{1 \le v \le n} (x_{\sigma_1} + \cdots + x_{\sigma_v})^+$$

in his study [35] on samples without replacements. Carleson also indicated by an heuristic argument that this work of Rosén might provide a new proof of our inequality 3.8.1.

As it turned out, Rosén, who was mainly interested in extending to samples without replacement certain classical limit theorems for samples with replacement, had the idea (quite natural in such an endeavor) to make use of Kolmogorov methods. This led us to try and extend even further these methods in the direction needed to establish the inequality 3.8.2. The outcome was the inequality of Proposition 3.7.2.

There is a further interesting remark made by Carleson in this context that we would like to present. To this end we need to introduce some notation.

For a given set of reals $x_1, x_2, \ldots, x_n$ we introduce identically distributed independent random variables $X_1, X_2, \ldots, X_n$ each of them taking the values $x_1, x_2, \ldots, x_n$ with equal probability $1/n$. A way to realize such a process is to take Ω as the space of all n-tuples $\omega = (i_1, i_2, \ldots, i_n)$ of numbers $1 \le i_v \le n$ $(v = 1, 2, \ldots, n)$, then assign to each ω probability $(1/n)^n$ and set

$$X_v(\omega) = x_{i_v}.$$

The probabilistic interpretation of the functions $\Phi_\nu(\sigma)$ and $X_\nu(\omega)$ is immediate. We can imagine an urn which contains n balls labeled $x_1, x_2, \ldots, x_n$. If we sample n times the contents of this urn we obtain $\Phi_1(\sigma), \Phi_2(\sigma), \ldots, \Phi_n(\sigma)$ if we do not put the balls back into the urn after each sampling and $X_1(\omega), X_2(\omega), \ldots, X_n(\omega)$ if we do.

Carleson conjectured that since the partial sums

3.8.3 $$\mathcal{O}_\nu(\sigma) = \Phi_1(\sigma) + \Phi_2(\sigma) + \cdots + \Phi_\nu(\sigma)$$

are more likely to stay closer to the sum $x_1 + x_2 + \cdots + x_n$ than the partial sums

3.8.4 $$S_\nu(\omega) = X_1(\omega) + X_2(\omega) + \cdots + X_\nu(\omega),$$

the L_p norms of the functions

$$\mathcal{O}_\nu^*(\sigma) = \max_{1 \le \mu \le \nu} |\mathcal{O}_\mu(\sigma)|$$

should be no worse than those of the functions

$$S_\nu^*(\omega) = \max_{1 \le \mu \le \nu} |S_\mu(\omega)|.$$

Carleson, to substantiate his remark, pointed out to us the following remarkable inequality of Hoeffding [16].

PROPOSITION 3.8.1. *If $\mathcal{O}_\nu(\sigma)$ and $S_\nu(\omega)$ are defined as in* 3.8.3, *and* 3.8.4, *then for any convex function $\Psi(x)$ and every $1 \le \nu \le n$ we have*

3.8.5 $$E(\Psi(\mathcal{O}_\nu)) \le E(\Psi(S_\nu));$$

more explicitly,

$$\frac{1}{n!}\sum_\sigma \Psi(x_{\sigma_1} + x_{\sigma_2} + \cdots + x_{\sigma_\nu}) \le \frac{1}{n^\nu}\sum_{i_1=1}\sum_{i_2=1}\cdots \sum_{i_\nu=1} \Psi(x_{i_1} + x_{i_2} + \cdots + x_{i_\nu}).$$

(The proof of this inequality is a pretty straightforward consequence of Jensen's inequality and will be omitted.)

It turns out that our Proposition 3.7.1 combined with 3.8.5 gives a reasonable verification of Carleson's conjecture.

In fact, if we multiply the inequality in 3.7.9 by λ^{p-1} and integrate we obtain $\forall\, p > 1$,

3.8.6 $$\int_\Omega [\mathcal{O}_m^*(\sigma)]^p\, dP \le \left(\frac{2p}{p-1}\right)^p \int_\Omega [\mathcal{O}_m(\sigma)]^p\, dP.$$

On the other hand, from Proposition 3.2.1 when

3.8.7 $$x_1 + x_2 + \cdots + x_n = 0$$

we easily get in a similar fashion $\forall\ \nu = 1, 2, \ldots, n$ and $\forall\ p > 1$,

3.8.8 $$\int_\Omega [S_\nu^*(\omega)]^p \, dP \le \left(\frac{p}{p-1}\right)^p \int_\Omega [S_\nu(\omega)]^p \, dP.$$

Hoeffding's inequality (3.8.5) for $\Psi(x) = x^p$ combined with 3.8.6 gives

3.8.9 $$\int_\Omega [\mathcal{O}_m^*(\sigma)]^p \, dP \le \left(\frac{2p}{p-1}\right)^p \int_\Omega [S_m(\omega)]^p \, dP.$$

Comparing 3.8.8 (for $\nu = m$) with 3.8.9 we see that the growths of the L_p norms of $\mathcal{O}_m^*$ and S_m^* as $p \to \infty$ may at most differ by a constant factor.

Actually, a sharper result was obtained by Rosén by quite different methods. Indeed, Rosén in [36] established an inequality of type 3.8.5, where $\mathcal{O}_\nu$ and S_ν are replaced by $\mathcal{O}_\nu^*$ and S_ν^*, respectively. Thus Carleson's conjecture holds in the strongest possible sense.

We shall terminate by making one additional remark. The integral

$$I_{2p}(\nu) = \int_\Omega |\Phi_1(\sigma) + \cdots + \Phi_\nu(\sigma)|^{2p} \, dP$$

can be written in the more suggestive form

$$I_{2p}(\nu) = \frac{1}{\binom{n}{\nu}} \sum_{1 \le i_1 < \cdots < i_\nu \le n} (x_{i_1} + \cdots + x_{i_\nu})^{2p}.$$

If we use the estimate of Proposition 3.5.1 with $X_1, X_2, \ldots, X_n$ equal to the first n Rademacher functions and $a_\nu = x_\nu$, we get, at least when the relation 3.8.7 holds,

$$\frac{1}{2^n} \sum_{\nu=0}^{n} \binom{n}{\nu} \left[\frac{1}{\binom{n}{\nu}} \sum_{1 \le i_1 < \cdots < i_\nu \le n} |x_{i_1} + x_{i_2} + \cdots + x_{i_\nu}|^{2p} \right]$$
$$\le \frac{(2p)!}{4^p p!} (x_1^2 + x_2^2 + \cdots + x_n^2)^p.$$

This shows that $I_{2p}(\nu)$ is in an "average" sense less than a constant

C_p times $(x_1^2 + x_2^2 + \cdots + x_n^2)^p$. It is not difficult to show actually that for every $v = 1, 2, \ldots, n$,

$$I_{2p}(v) \leq C_p\left(\sum_{v=1}^{n} x_v^2\right)^p.$$

We can thus deduce the inequality

3.8.10

$$\frac{1}{n!}\sum_{\sigma} \max_{1 \leq v \leq n} (x_{\sigma_1} + x_{\sigma_2} + \cdots + x_{\sigma_v})^{2p} \leq C_p(x_1^2 + x_2^2 + \cdots + x_n^2)^p.$$

When 3.8.7 is not assumed, from the above inequality we deduce

3.8.11 $$\frac{1}{n!}\sum_{\sigma} \max_{1 \leq v \leq n} (x_{\sigma_1} + \cdots + x_{\sigma_v} - vT)^{2p} \leq C_p\left(\sum_{v=1}^{n} x_v^2\right)^p,$$

where we have set

$$T = \frac{1}{n}\sum_{v=1}^{n} x_v.$$

Now, let $\Phi_1(x), \Phi_2(x), \ldots, \Phi_n(x)$ be an orthonormal set on some measure space $(\Omega, \mathscr{F}, \mu)$ and let $a_1, a_2, \ldots, a_n$ be real numbers. Suppose $\Phi_1, \Phi_2, \ldots, \Phi_n$ are all bounded by a constant M. Then from 3.8.11 by setting $x_v = a_v\Phi_v(x)$ and integrating upon Ω we get

3.8.12 $$\frac{1}{n!}\sum_{\sigma} \int_{\Omega} \max_{1 \leq v \leq n} (a_{\sigma_1}\Phi_{\sigma_1}(x) + \cdots + a_{\sigma_v}\Phi_{\sigma_v}(x) - \frac{v}{n}f(x))^{2p}\, d\mu$$

$$\leq C_p M^{2p}\left(\int_{\Omega} [f(x)]^2\, dx\right)^p,$$

where we have set

$$f(x) = a_1\Phi_1(x) + a_2\Phi_2(x) + \cdots + a_n\Phi_n(x).$$

In other words, we have obtained for rearrangements inequalities parallel to those obtained by Zygmund and Paley for changes of signs. This suggests that for the case of random rearrangements it should be possible to develop a theory parallel to that which Zygmund, Paley, and Salem have developed for random changes of signs. Finally, we would like to mention that using the inequality 3.8.12 it is possible to improve the estimates obtained by Greenhall in [14]. Such results can be found in [12], where further simplifications have also been obtained in the proof of some of the combinatorial inequalities established in this chapter.

4

CARLESON'S "log log *n*" RESULT

4.1 PRELIMINARIES

In the fall of 1965, L. Carleson proved what is perhaps the deepest of the almost everywhere convergence theorems, the almost everywhere convergence of Fourier series,

4.1.1 $$\sum_{\nu=0}^{\infty} (a_\nu \cos \nu x + b_\nu \sin \nu x),$$

when

4.1.2 $$\sum_{\nu=0}^{\infty} (a_\nu^2 + b_\nu^2) < \infty.$$

Unfortunately, to this date, this theorem can only be reached via a highly technical and involved path. For this reason, we shall present here only the first result obtained by Carleson in his investigation—the a.e. convergence of the series in 4.1.1 under the stronger condition

4.1.3 $$\sum_{\nu=2}^{\infty} (a_\nu^2 + b_\nu^2)(\log \log \nu)^2 < \infty.$$

In the process of doing so, we hope to give at least the flavor of Carleson's methods. Also, we shall need to develop the basic tools that are essential for a further study of Carleson's investigations.

In order to understand the significance of the result we shall present here, it is worthwhile to point out that although the a.e. convergence of 4.1.1 under the sole condition 4.1.2 was conjectured by Luzin [28] as early as 1922, for many years the theorem of Kolmogorov and Seliverstov [26], which asserted the a.e. convergence of 4.1.1 under the assumption

4.1.4 $$\sum_{\nu=1}^{\infty} (a_\nu^2 + b_\nu^2) \log \nu < \infty,$$

had resisted all attempts at improvement and was believed by many to be best possible.

To establish our notation, let $f(x)$ be defined and periodic of period 2π in $(-\infty, +\infty)$ and integrable in $[-\pi, +\pi]$. We set

$$S_n(x, f) = \sum_{\nu=0}^{n} (a_\nu \cos \nu x + b_\nu \sin \nu x)$$

with

$$a_n = \frac{1}{\pi} \int_{-\pi}^{\pi} f(t) \cos nt\, dt, \qquad b_n = \frac{1}{\pi} \int_{-\pi}^{\pi} f(t) \sin nt\, dt.$$

It was well known, even before Carleson's work, that to establish the convergence of 4.1.1 under a hypothesis of the type

4.1.5 $$\sum_{n} (a_n^2 + b_n^2)\lambda_n^2 < \infty,$$

where λ_n is any fixed nondecreasing sequence tending to ∞, we need only establish that

4.1.6 $$S_n(x, f) = O(\lambda_n) \quad \text{a.e.} \qquad \forall \quad f \in L_2(-\pi, \pi).$$

In other words,

4.1.7 $$\Gamma^*(x, f) = \sup_{n} \frac{|S_n(x, f)|}{\lambda_n} < \infty \quad \text{a.e.} \qquad \forall \quad f \in L_2(-\pi, \pi).$$

This fact is an immediate consequence of the continuity principle of Section 1.2. Indeed, from 4.1.7, it follows that, for some constant $c > 0$, we must have

$$m\{x \in [-\pi, \pi] : \Gamma^*(x, f) > \lambda\}$$
$$\leq \frac{c}{\lambda^2} \int_{-\pi}^{\pi} |f|^2\, dx \qquad \forall \quad f \in L_2(-\pi, \pi),$$

and for all $\lambda > 0$.

This then implies that, if we set

$$\Omega^*(x, f) = \limsup_{n \to \infty} \frac{|S_n(x, f)|}{\lambda_n},$$

then we must also have

$$m\{x \in [-\pi, \pi] : \Omega^*(x, f) > \lambda\} \leq \frac{c}{\lambda^2} \int_{-\pi}^{\pi} |f|^2 \, dx.$$

On the other hand, we easily see that $\Omega^*(x, f)$ is not affected if we delete from $\sum_{\nu=0}^{\infty} (a_\nu \cos \nu x + b_\nu \sin \nu x)$ any finite number of terms. This implies that

$$m\{x \in [-\pi, \pi] : \Omega^*(x, f) > \lambda\} \leq \frac{c}{\lambda^2} \int_{-\pi}^{\pi} |f - S_n(x, f)|^2 \, dx \qquad \forall \quad n.$$

Consequently,

$$m\{x \in [-\pi, \pi] : \Omega^*(x, f) > \lambda\} = 0 \qquad \forall \quad \lambda > 0.$$

In other words, in the presence of 4.1.7, we must necessarily have

4.1.8 $$\lim_{n \to \infty} \frac{S_n(x, f)}{\lambda_n} = 0 \quad \text{a.e.} \qquad \forall \quad f \in L_2(-\pi, \pi).$$

Suppose now that f is not only in $L_2(-\pi, \pi)$ but satisfies 4.1.5; then the series

$$\sum_{n=0}^{\infty} (a_n \cos nx + b_n \sin nx)\lambda_n$$

is the Fourier expansion of a function g that is square integrable in $[-\pi, \pi]$, and if we set

$$S_n(x, g) = \sum_{\nu=0}^{n} (a_\nu \cos \nu x + b_\nu \sin \nu x)\lambda_\nu,$$

we have, setting

$$S_{-1}(x, g) = 0:$$

4.1.9 $$S_n(x, f) = \sum_{\nu=0}^{n-1} \left(\frac{1}{\lambda_\nu} - \frac{1}{\lambda_{\nu+1}}\right) S_\nu(x, g) + \frac{S_n(x, g)}{\lambda_n}.$$

By 4.1.8,

$$\frac{S_n(x, g)}{\lambda_n} \to 0 \quad \text{a.e.}$$

Furthermore, since

$$\sum_{\nu=0}^{\infty}\left(\frac{1}{\lambda_\nu}-\frac{1}{\lambda_{\nu+1}}\right)\int_{-\pi}^{\pi}|S_\nu(x,g)|\,dx \le \frac{1}{\lambda_0}\left[\int_{-\pi}^{\pi}[g(x)]^2\,dx\right]^{1/2},$$

we deduce that the series

$$\sum_{\nu=0}^{\infty}\left(\frac{1}{\lambda_\nu}-\frac{1}{\lambda_{\nu+1}}\right)S_\nu(x,g)$$

is a.e. absolutely convergent.

Combining these last two observations with 4.1.9, we readily obtain the a.e. convergence of the partial sums of $S_n(x, f)$.

This given, we shall concentrate on proving

$$S_n(x,f)=\frac{1}{\pi}\int_{-\pi}^{\pi} f(x-t)\frac{\sin(n+\frac{1}{2})t}{2\sin t/2}\,dt = 0\,(\log\log n)$$

a.e. as $n \to \infty$.

A further reduction of the problem is still possible. Indeed, note that we can write

$$\frac{\sin(n+\frac{1}{2})t}{2\sin t/2}=\frac{\sin nt}{t}+\cos nt+\sin nt\left(\frac{1}{2\tan t/2}-\frac{1}{t}\right).$$

Thus

$$S_n(x,f)=\frac{1}{\pi}\int_{-\pi}^{\pi} f(x-t)\frac{\sin nt}{t}\,dt+\frac{1}{\pi}\int_{-\pi}^{\pi} f(x-t)\cos nt\,dt$$
$$+\frac{1}{\pi}\int_{-\pi}^{\pi} f(x-t)\left(\frac{1}{2\tan t/2}-\frac{1}{t}\right)\sin nt\,dt.$$

We see then that, since $[1/(2\tan t/2)] - (1/t)$ is bounded and continuous in $[-\pi, \pi]$, we have

$$\left|S_n(x,f)-\frac{1}{\pi}\int_{-\pi}^{\pi} f(x-t)\frac{\sin nt}{t}\,dt\right| \le c\int_{-\pi}^{\pi}|f(t)|\,dt.\dagger$$

Furthermore, let

$$F(x)=\begin{cases} f(x) & |x| \le 2\pi, \\ 0 & |x| > 2\pi. \end{cases}$$

† To avoid keeping track of the actual values of constants, in this chapter an inequality of the form $|g(x)| \le c$ is to be read as follows: There is a constant c such that $|g(x)| \le c$. If c depends on the values of some parameters, this will be indicated by subscripts.

Then, for $|x| \leq \pi$,

$$\left| \frac{1}{\pi} \int_{-\pi}^{\pi} f(x-t) \frac{\sin nt}{t} \, dt - \frac{1}{\pi} \int_{-\infty}^{+\infty} F(x-t) \frac{\sin nt}{t} \, dt \right| \leq \frac{1}{\pi^2} \int_{-2\pi}^{2\pi} |f(t)| \, dt.$$

Combining these observations, we see that all we need to show is the following. Given any square-integrable function $F(x)$ supported by an interval ω, then for almost all x in the mid-half of ω,

$$\sup_{n \geq 2} \left| \frac{\frac{1}{\pi} \int_{-\infty}^{+\infty} F(t) \frac{\sin n(x-t)}{x-t} \, dt}{\log \log n} \right| < \infty.$$

For a given function f, the expression

4.1.10 $$H(x, f) = \frac{1}{\pi} \int_{-\infty}^{+\infty} \frac{f(t) \, dt}{x - t}$$

is to be interpreted as

4.1.11 $$H(x, f) = \lim_{\epsilon \to 0} H_\epsilon(x, f),$$

where

$$H_\epsilon(x, f) = \frac{1}{\pi} \int_{|x-t| \geq \epsilon} \frac{f(t) \, dt}{x - t}.$$

The function $H(x, f)$ is called the "Hilbert transform" of f. It can be shown that if f is integrable in $(-\infty, +\infty)$ the limit in 4.1.11 exists a.e. and when $f \in L_p(-\infty, +\infty)(p > 1)$ $H(x, f)$ is also in $L_p(-\infty, +\infty)$.

We can thus write

$$\frac{1}{\pi} \int_{-\pi}^{\pi} F(t) \frac{\sin n(x-t)}{x-t} \, dt = \frac{e^{inx}}{2i} H(x, Fe^{int}) - \frac{e^{-inx}}{2i} H(x, Fe^{-int}).$$

It should be apparent, by this formula, that in our study, the Hilbert transform should play an essential role. Indeed, this is the case, and in the next few sections we shall have to establish the basic properties of this very important operator and of related operators.

4.2 THE HARDY–LITTLEWOOD FUNCTION

Here and in the following $f(x)$ will denote a real-valued function defined in $(-\infty, +\infty)$ which, to simplify our exposition, will be assumed integrable and of compact support. Of course, these assumptions on f are more than is needed to establish some of our preliminary results, but the generality obtained will be sufficient for all our later applications.

Two operators related to $H(x, f)$ and $H_\epsilon(x, f)$ are

$$P_y(x, f) = \frac{1}{\pi}\int_{-\infty}^{+\infty} \frac{f(t)y\,dt}{(x-t)^2 + y^2},$$

$$Q_y(x, f) = \frac{1}{\pi}\int_{-\infty}^{+\infty} f(t)\frac{x-t}{(x-t)^2 + y^2}\,dt.$$

These, for $y > 0$, are the "Poisson" and "conjugate Poisson" operators for the upper-half plane, familiar in potential theory. We see that at least formally

$$H(x, f) = Q_0(x, f).$$

More precisely, we can show

4.2.1 $$\lim_{y\to 0}\,[H_y(x, f) - Q_y(x, f)] = 0 \quad \text{a.e.}$$

To this end, we write

$$|H_y(x, f) - Q_y(x, f)| \le \frac{1}{\pi}\int_{|x-t|>y} |f(t)|\frac{y^2}{|x-t|\,[(x-t)^2 + y^2]}\,dt + \frac{1}{\pi}\int_{|x-t|\le y} \frac{|f(t)|\,y}{(x-t)^2 + y^2}\,dt.$$

Therefore,

4.2.2 $$|H_y(x, f) - Q_y(x, f)| \le P_y(x, |f|).$$

Using the relations

$$\int_{y\le |t|\le m} \frac{dt}{t} = 0 \qquad \text{and} \qquad \int_{-m}^{m} \frac{t\,dt}{t^2 + y^2} = 0,$$

we also easily deduce that

4.2.3 $$|H_y(x, f) - Q_y(x, f)| \le \frac{1}{\pi}\int_{-\infty}^{+\infty} |f(t) - f(x)|\frac{y}{(x-t)^2 + y^2}\,dt.$$

Thus 4.2.1 could be established by showing that

$$\lim_{y\to 0} \frac{1}{\pi}\int_{-\infty}^{+\infty} |f(t) - f(x)| \frac{y}{(x-t)^2 + y^2}\, dt = 0 \quad \text{a.e.}$$

This is a classical result we should want to derive. At any rate, it is clear then that 4.2.1 does hold for continuous $f(x)$.

Of great importance in our later considerations are estimates concerning the function

4.2.4 $$H^*(x, f) = \sup_{\epsilon>0} |H_\epsilon(x, f)|.$$

This function is referred to as the "maximal Hilbert transform" of f. To estimate $H^*(x, f)$ and to prove 4.2.1 for general $f(x)$, it is apparent, in view of 4.2.2, that we should study the function

$$\sup_{y>0} P_y(x, |f|).$$

To see show this function can be estimated, observe that the kernel

$$k_y(t) = \frac{1}{\pi}\frac{y}{t^2 + y^2}$$

has the following basic properties:

4.2.5 (a) $k(t) = k(-t) \geq 0 \quad \forall \ t;$

(b) $k(t_1) \geq k(t_2) \quad$ when $0 \leq t_1 \leq t_2;$

(c) $\displaystyle\int_{-\infty}^{+\infty} k(t)\, dt = 1.$

For such a kernel, the convolution operator

$$k(x, f) = \int_{-\infty}^{+\infty} f(x - t)k(t)\, dt = \int_{-\infty}^{+\infty} f(t)k(x - t)\, dt$$

can be majorized by an operator depending only on f. This is seen as follows. Note that we can write

$$k(x, f) = \int_{-\infty}^{+\infty} f(x - t) \int_0^{\infty} \chi(k(t), \lambda)\, d\lambda\, dt,$$

where, as we have usually done,

$$\chi(a, b) = \begin{cases} 1 & \text{if } a \geq b, \\ 0 & \text{if } a < b. \end{cases}$$

In view of properties 4.2.5(a) and (b),

$$\left|\int_{-\infty}^{+\infty} f(x-t)\chi(k(t),\lambda)\,dt\right| \leq \int_{-\infty}^{+\infty} \chi(k(t),\lambda)\,dt \sup_{h>0} \frac{1}{2h}\int_{-h}^{h} |f(x-t)|\,dt.$$

We can thus conclude that

THEOREM 4.2.1. *If $k(t)$ is any kernel with the properties in 4.2.5, then*

$$|k(x,f)| \leq \theta(x,f),$$

where

$$\theta(x,f) = \sup_{h>0} \frac{1}{2h}\int_{-h}^{h} |f(x-t)|\,dt.$$

The function $\theta(x,f)$ is referred to as the "Hardy–Littlewood maximal function of f." It is apparent from the consideration above that $\theta(x,f)$ should turn out to be a basic tool in our study. A crucial estimate is given by

THEOREM 4.2.2. *If f is integrable in $(-\infty, +\infty)$ and $\lambda > 0$,*

4.2.6 $$m\{x : \theta(x,f) > \lambda\} \leq \frac{2}{\lambda}\int_{-\infty}^{+\infty} |f(x)|\,dx.$$

PROOF. Set first

$$\theta_\epsilon(x,f) = \sup_{h\geq\epsilon} \frac{1}{2h}\int_{-h}^{h} |f(x-t)|\,dt.$$

We easily deduce, using the compactness of the support of f, that for each $\lambda > 0$, the set

$$E = \{x : \theta_\epsilon(x,f) \geq \lambda\}$$

is also compact.

Furthermore, the class of intervals I such that

4.2.7 $$\int_I |f(t)|\,dt \geq \lambda|I|$$

clearly covers E. Thus a finite family $\mathscr{A}$ of such intervals covers E as well.

However, we do have the following:

INTERVAL SELECTION LEMMA 4.2.1. *From any finite family $\mathscr{A}$ of intervals of the real axis, it is always possible to select a finite subfamily $I_1, I_2, \ldots, I_n$ of disjoint intervals such that*

4.2.8 $$m\Big(\bigcup_{I \in \mathscr{A}} I\Big) \leq 2 \sum_{\nu=1}^{n} m(I_\nu).$$

Accepting for a moment the validity of this statement, we immediately deduce that for some disjoint intervals I_ν satisfying 4.2.7 we have

$$m\{x : \theta_\epsilon(x, f) \geq \lambda\} \leq 2 \sum_{\nu=1}^{n} m(I_\nu) \leq \frac{2}{\lambda} \sum_{\nu=1}^{n} \int_{I_\nu} |f(t)|\, dt$$
$$\leq \frac{2}{\lambda} \int_{-\infty}^{+\infty} |f(t)|\, dt.$$

This relation gives 4.2.6, upon passing to the limit, as $\epsilon \to 0$.

We now proceed with the proof of Lemma 4.2.1. Let such a family $\mathscr{A}$ be given. We observe that we can, removing a few intervals from $\mathscr{A}$, if necessary, assume that no interval of $\mathscr{A}$ is contained in the union of the remaining ones. If this is the case, when the intervals of $\mathscr{A}$ are labeled

$$J_k = [\alpha_k, \beta_k] \qquad k = 1, 2, \ldots$$

according to the size of their left end points, we must have

(a) $\alpha_k < \alpha_{k+1}$;

(b) $\beta_{2k-1} < \alpha_{2k+1}$;

(c) $\beta_{2k} < \alpha_{2k+2}$.

Indeed, if for some k, $\alpha_k = \alpha_{k+1}$, one of the two intervals J_k, J_{k+1} contains the other. Similarly, if $\beta_{2k-1} \geq \alpha_{2k+1}$, then one of the intervals

$$J_{2k-1}, \quad J_{2k}, \quad J_{2k+1}$$

is contained in the union of the other two. An analogous situation occurs if (c) is violated.

We thus conclude that the odd-numbered intervals, as well as the even-numbered ones, are disjoint. This means that we can take

$I_k = J_{2k-1}$ or $I_k = J_{2k}$ for

$$m(\bigcup_{I \in \mathscr{A}}) \leq m(\sum_k I_{2k-1}) + m(\sum_k I_{2k}).$$

REMARK 4.2.1. Lemma 4.2.1, which is easily recognized as a simplified version of Vitali's famed covering lemma, is apparently due to W. H. Young.† It is interesting to point out that although it is rather easy to prove, in the applications it seems to be just as powerful as Vitali's original lemma.

REMARK 4.2.2. Theorem 4.2.2 can be proved in many other ways. Perhaps the most commonly known proof is obtained via the "sunrise lemma" of F. Riesz. Setting

$$\theta^+(x, f) = \max_{h>0} \left(\frac{1}{h}\int_0^h f(x + t)\, dt\right)^+,$$

we obtain via Riesz's lemma,

4.2.9 $$\int_{\{x : \theta^+(x, f) > 0\}} f\, dx \geq 0.$$

This inequality, upon replacing f by $f - \lambda\chi(x)$, where $\chi(x)$ is the indicator of a sufficiently large interval, gives

4.2.10 $$m\{x : \theta^+(x, f) > \lambda\} \leq \frac{1}{\lambda}\int_{\{x : \theta^+(x, f) > \lambda\}} f(x)\, dx,$$

from which 4.2.6 can be easily deduced.

The details of this proof can be found in Zygmund [43], Vol. 1. It might be of interest to point out here that the inequality 4.2.9, which of course resembles the maximal ergodic inequality of Section 2.2, can also be established by methods similar to those used there. We shall give the general outline of this further proof.

Let $h_0 > 0$ be fixed. We define for each x

$$\varphi(x, f) = \max_{0 \leq h \leq h_0} \left(\int_0^h f(x + t)\, dt\right)^+.$$

For a given $\delta > 0$, we set

$$E_\delta = \left\{x : \varphi(x, f) = \max_{\delta \leq h \leq h_0} \left(\int_0^h f(x + t)\, dt\right)^+ > 0\right\}.$$

† We owe this reference to E. Bishop.

Clearly, as $\delta \to 0$, $E_\delta \uparrow E_0 = \{x : \varphi(x, f) > 0\}$. Note that for all $\delta \le h \le h_0$,

$$\int_0^\delta f(x + t)\,dt + \varphi(x + \delta, f) \ge \int_0^h f(x + t)\,dt.$$

Thus, for $x \in E_\delta$,

$$\int_0^\delta f(x + t)\,dt \ge \varphi(x, f) - \varphi(x + \delta, f).$$

Integrating over E_δ, we get

4.2.11 $$\int_{E_\delta} \left\{ \int_0^\delta f(x + t)\,dt \right\} dx \ge \int_{E_\delta} \left\{ \varphi(x, f) - \varphi(x + \delta, f) \right\} dx.$$

Now observe that

$$\left| \int_{E_\delta} f(x)\,dx - \frac{1}{\delta} \int_{E_\delta} \left(\int_0^\delta f(x + t)\,dt \right) dx \right| \le \frac{1}{\delta} \int_0^\delta \left\{ \int_{-\infty}^{+\infty} |f(x) - f(x + t)|\,dx \right\} dt.$$

Thus

4.2.12 $$\int_{E_0} f(x)\,dx = \lim_{\delta \to 0} \frac{1}{\delta} \int_{E_\delta} \left\{ \int_0^\delta f(x + t)\,dt \right\} dx.$$

On the other hand, since $\varphi(x, f)$ vanishes outside of E_0,

4.2.13 $$\int_{E_\delta} \{\varphi(x, f) - \varphi(x + \delta, f)\}\,dx \ge \int_{E_\delta} \varphi(x, f)\,dx - \int_{E_0} \varphi(x + \delta, f)\,dx = -\int_{E_0 - E_\delta} \varphi(x, f)\,dx.$$

However, since in $E_0 - E_\delta$

$$\varphi(x, f) = \int_0^h f(x + t)\,dt \qquad \text{for some } h < \delta,$$

we do get there

$$\left|\frac{1}{\delta}\varphi(x, f) - f(x)\right| \leq \frac{1}{\delta}\int_0^\delta |f(x+t) - f(x)|\, dt + |f(x)|.$$

Combining this relation with 4.2.11, 4.2.12, and 4.2.13 as $\delta \to 0$, 4.2.10 follows readily upon letting $h_0 \to \infty$.

We are in a position now to prove the relation 4.2.1. Indeed, the proof should, by now, appear quite standard. We set

$$\Omega(x, f) = \limsup_{y \to 0} |H_y(x, f) - Q_y(x, f)|.$$

From 4.2.2 and Theorems 4.2.1 and 4.2.2 we get

$$m\{x : \Omega(x, f) > \epsilon\} \leq \frac{2}{\epsilon}\int_{-\infty}^{+\infty} |f(x)|\, dx \qquad \forall \quad \epsilon > 0.$$

The inequality in 4.2.3 tells us that $\Omega(x, f)$ is not affected if we subtract from f any continuous function $f_0(x)$ of compact support. Thus we also have

$$m\{x : \Omega(x, f) > \epsilon\} \leq \frac{2}{\epsilon}\int_{-\infty}^{+\infty} |f(x) - f_0(x)|\, dx.$$

From the arbitrariness of $f_0(x)$, we then deduce that

$$m\{x : \Omega(x, f) > \epsilon\} = 0 \qquad \forall \quad \epsilon > 0.$$

In other words,

$$\Omega(x, f) = 0 \quad \text{a.e.}$$

We conclude this section by establishing some further auxiliary inequalities.

THEOREM 4.2.3. *If f is in L_p $(p > 1)$, then*

4.2.14 $$\int_{-\infty}^{+\infty} [\theta(x, f)]^p\, dx \leq \frac{p2^{p+1}}{p-1}\int_{-\infty}^{+\infty} |f|^p\, dx.$$

If $|f| \log^+|f|$ is integrable, then

4.2.15 $$\int_{-\infty}^{+\infty} (\theta(x, f) - 2)^+\, dx \leq 4\int_{-\infty}^{+\infty} |f| \log^+|f|\, dx.$$

PROOF. We set

$$f = f_\lambda + f^\lambda,$$

where

$$f^{\lambda} = \begin{cases} f & \text{when } |f| \leq \lambda, \\ 0 & \text{otherwise.} \end{cases}$$

Clearly

$$\theta(x, f^{\lambda}) \leq \lambda;$$

thus

$$m\{x : \theta(x, f) > 2\lambda\} \leq m\{x : \theta(x, f_{\lambda}) > \lambda\},$$

and 4.2.6 gives

4.2.16 $$m\{x : \theta(x, f) > 2\lambda\} \leq \frac{2}{\lambda} \int_{-\infty}^{+\infty} |f_{\lambda}(x)| \, dx.$$

This estimate implies both 4.2.14 and 4.2.15. Indeed, if we simply integrate 4.2.16 with respect to λ from 1 to ∞, we get 4.2.15, while if we multiply 4.2.16 by λ^{p-1} and integrate from 0 to ∞, we get 4.2.14.

Note. Similar estimates can be obtained by working with 4.2.10 via the strong estimate theorem (Theorem 2.2.3).

REMARK 4.2.3. At this moment it is worthwhile to observe that the operators $H_{\epsilon}(x, f)$, $Q_y(x, f)$, and $P_y(x, f)$ are all of the type

4.2.17 $$K(x, f) = \int_{-\infty}^{+\infty} K(x - t) f(t) \, dt,$$

with

4.2.18 $$\int_{-\infty}^{+\infty} |K(t)| \, dt < \infty.$$

Such operators transform square-integrable functions into square-integrable functions. Indeed we have

THEOREM 4.2.4. *Let $K(x, f)$ be defined by* 4.2.17 *with $K(t)$ satisfying* 4.2.18. *If f is in L_p, with $p \geq 1$, then $K(x, f)$ is also in L_p and*

4.2.19 $$\left[\int_{-\infty}^{+\infty} [K(x, f)]^p \, dx\right]^{1/p} \leq \int_{-\infty}^{+\infty} |K(x)| \, dx \left[\int_{-\infty}^{+\infty} |f(x)|^p \, dx\right]^{1/p}.$$

PROOF. An application of Hölder's inequality gives

$$[K(x, f)]^p \leq \int_{-\infty}^{+\infty} |K(x - t)| |f(t)|^p \, dt \left[\int_{-\infty}^{+\infty} |K(t)| \, dt \right]^{p-1}.$$

Integrating with respect to x, by Fubini's theorem, we get

$$\int_{-\infty}^{+\infty} [K(x, f)]^p \, dx \leq \int_{-\infty}^{+\infty} |f(t)|^p \, dt \left[\int_{-\infty}^{+\infty} |K(t)| \, dt \right]^p,$$

and this of course is 4.2.19.

COROLLARY 4.2.1. *If $f \in L_p(-\infty, +\infty)$, then*

4.2.20 $$\int_{-\infty}^{+\infty} |P_y(x, f)|^p \, dx \leq \int_{-\infty}^{+\infty} |f(x)|^p \, dx.$$

Indeed we also have

4.2.21 $$\lim_{y \to 0} \int_{-\infty}^{+\infty} |P_y(x, f) - f(x)|^p \, dx = 0,$$

as well as

4.2.22 $$\lim_{y \to 0} P_y(x, f) = f(x) \qquad \text{a.e. in } (-\infty, +\infty).$$

PROOF. 4.2.20 clearly follows from 4.2.19 since

$$\frac{1}{\pi} \int_{-\infty}^{+\infty} \frac{y}{x^2 + y^2} \, dx = 1.$$

To complete this proof, note that both 4.2.21 and 4.2.22 are immediate when $f(x)$ is a continuous function of compact support.

This given, for a fixed $\epsilon > 0$, let f_ϵ be continuous and of compact support and so close to f, in the L_p sense, that

$$\int_{-\infty}^{+\infty} |f_\epsilon(x) - f(x)|^p \, dx < \epsilon.$$

We then get, using obvious abbreviations,

$$\|P_y(f) - f\|_p \leq \|P_y(f - f_\epsilon)\|_p + \|P_y(f_\epsilon) - f_\epsilon\|_p + \|f_\epsilon - f\|_p.$$

So that, by 4.2.20,

$$\|P_y(f) - f\|_p \leq 2\|f - f_\epsilon\|_p + \|P_y(f_\epsilon) - f_\epsilon\|_p.$$

We deduce then that

$$\limsup_{y\to 0} \| P_y(f) - f \|_p \le 2\epsilon.$$

This implies 4.2.21, since ϵ can be chosen as small as we please.

The result in 4.2.22 is established by a method that should be quite familiar at this point. We simply set

$$\Omega(x, f) = \lim_{y\to 0} |P_y(x, f) - f(x)|,$$

then observe that

$$|\Omega(x, f)| \le \theta(x, f) + |f(x)|.$$

Thereafter the proof of 4.2.22 is entirely equivalent to the proof of 4.2.1.

Theorem 4.2.4 does not yield an inequality for $\| H_\epsilon(f) \|_p$ or $\| Q_y(f) \|_p$, since

$$\frac{1}{\pi}\int_{-\infty}^{+\infty} \frac{t}{t^2 + y^2}\, dt = \frac{1}{\pi}\int_{|t|\ge\epsilon} \frac{dt}{|t|} = \infty;$$

thus we can get no information at all concerning $H(x, f)$ itself. The remarkable fact is that for $Q_y(f)$ as well as $H_\epsilon(f)$, bounds can be obtained that are independent of y and ϵ, respectively. But the proofs, as we shall see, have to follow a somewhat more tortuous path.

4.3 EXISTENCE AND MAXIMAL ESTIMATES FOR THE HILBERT TRANSFORM

In this section we shall show that the limit

$$H(x, f) = \lim_{\epsilon\to 0} \int_{|x-t|>\epsilon} f(t)\frac{dt}{x - t}$$

exists almost everywhere, and derive estimates for the function

$$H^*(x, f) = \sup_{\epsilon>0} |H_\epsilon(x, f)| = \sup_{\epsilon>0} \left| \int_{|x-t|>\epsilon} \frac{f(t)\, dt}{x - t} \right|.$$

The crucial tool here will be a little known but very remarkable lemma due to Loomis [27].

LOOMIS' LEMMA 4.3.1. *Let $m_1, m_2, \ldots, m_n$ be positive constants and $x_1 < x_2 < \cdots < x_n$ be given reals and set*

$$g(x) = \sum_{\nu=1}^{n} \frac{m_\nu}{x - x_\nu}.$$

We have

4.3.1 $$m\{x : g(x) \geq \lambda\} = m\{x : g(x) \leq -\lambda\} = \frac{1}{\lambda} \sum_{\nu=1}^{n} m_\nu.$$

PROOF. Since $g(x)$ is monotone decreasing in each interval $(x_\nu, x_{\nu+1})$ and tends to infinity as x decreases to x_ν, for each ν, we must have

4.3.2 $$m\{x : g(x) \geq \lambda\} = \sum_{\nu=1}^{n} (a_\nu(\lambda) - x_\nu),$$

where $a_1(\lambda), a_2(\lambda), \ldots, a_n(\lambda)$ are the roots of the equation

4.3.3 $$g(x) = \lambda.$$

Multiplying both sides of 4.3.3 by $\prod_{\nu=1}^{n} (x - x_\nu)$, we get that $a_1(\lambda), a_2(\lambda), \ldots, a_n(\lambda)$ are the roots of the polynomial

$$\lambda \prod_{\nu=1}^{n} (x - x_\nu) - \sum_{\nu=1}^{n} m_\nu \sum_{\mu=1}^{n}{}^{(\nu)} (x - x_\mu).$$

After dividing by λ, the coefficient of x^{n-1} then gives

$$\sum_{\nu=1}^{n} a_\nu(\lambda) = \sum_{\nu=1}^{n} x_\nu + \frac{1}{\lambda} \sum_{\nu=1}^{n} m_\nu.$$

Substituting this relation in 4.3.2, we get 4.3.1. A similar argument yields the result for $\{x : g(x) \leq -\lambda\}$.

We are finally in a position to deduce the basic estimate on $H^*(x, f)$.

THEOREM 4.3.1. *For any integrable f, we have*

4.3.4 $$m\{x : H^*(x, f) > \lambda\} \leq \frac{c}{\lambda} \int_{-\infty}^{+\infty} |f| \, dx.$$

PROOF. We can assume that $f \geq 0$. Indeed if 4.3.4 holds for nonnegative f, the familiar decomposition $f = f^+ - f^-$ together

with

$$m\{x : H^*(x, f) > \lambda\}$$
$$\leq m\left\{x : H^*(x, f^+) > \frac{\lambda}{2}\right\} + m\left\{x : H^*(x, f^-) > \frac{\lambda}{2}\right\}$$

yields the result for general f.

For convenience, if I is a finite interval of the real axis, we let ${}^cI$ denote the complement of I and $c(I)$ denote the center of I.

Then set

$$E_\epsilon^+ = \left\{x : \sup_{\eta \geq \epsilon} H_\eta(x, f) \geq \frac{\lambda}{\pi}\right\},$$

$$E_\epsilon^- = \left\{x : \sup_{\eta \geq \epsilon} - H_\eta(x, f) \geq \frac{\lambda}{\pi}\right\}.$$

Using the compactness of the support of f, we see that for each $\lambda > 0$, the set E_ϵ^+ is compact. In view of the definition of E_ϵ^+, the intervals I for which

4.3.5 $$\int_{{}^cI} \frac{f(t)\,dt}{c(I) - t} \geq \lambda$$

cover E_ϵ^+. Thus a finite number of these intervals cover E_ϵ^+ as well. By the interval selection lemma (Lemma 4.2.1), we can pick disjoint intervals $I_1, I_2, \ldots, I_n$ such that

4.3.6 $$m(E_\epsilon^+) \leq 2 \sum_{\nu=1}^{n} m(I_\nu)$$

and

4.3.7 $$\int_{{}^cI_\nu} \frac{f(t)\,dt}{c(I_\nu) - t} \geq \lambda.$$

Since the functions of t, $1/(x - t)$, for $|x - t| \geq \epsilon$, are equicontinuous, given any $\delta > 0$, we can find a decomposition of the real axis into small intervals σ such that for each ν,

4.3.8 $$\left| \int_{{}^cI_\nu} \frac{f(t)\,dt}{c(I_\nu) - t} - \sum_{\sigma \notin I_\nu} \frac{\int_\sigma f(t)\,dt}{c(I_\nu) - c(\sigma)} \right| < \delta\lambda.$$

Now set

$$g(x) = \sum_{\sigma} \frac{\int_{\sigma} f(t)\,dt}{x - c(\sigma)}, \qquad g_{\nu}(x) = \sum_{\sigma \in I_{\nu}} \frac{\int_{\sigma} f(t)\,dt}{x - c(\sigma)}.$$

The function

$$g(x) - g_{\nu}(x) = \sum_{\sigma \notin I_{\nu}} \frac{\int_{\sigma} f(t)\,dt}{x - c(\sigma)}$$

is clearly decreasing in I_{ν}. By 4.3.8 and 4.3.7, this function is greater than $(1 - \delta)\lambda$ for $x = c(I_{\nu})$, and therefore it will stay greater than this quantity throughout the left half of I_{ν}. We thus deduce that

$$\sum_{\nu=1}^{n} \frac{1}{2} m(I_{\nu}) \leq m\left\{x : g(x) > \frac{\lambda}{2}(1 - \delta)\right\} + \sum_{\nu=1}^{n} m\left\{x : g_{\nu}(x) < -\frac{\lambda}{2}(1 - \delta)\right\}.$$

Loomis' lemma then gives

$$\sum_{\nu=1}^{n} \frac{1}{2} m(I_{\nu}) \leq \frac{2}{\lambda(1 - \delta)} \sum_{\sigma} \int_{\sigma} f(t)\,dt + \sum_{\nu=1}^{n} \frac{2}{\lambda(1 - \delta)} \sum_{\sigma \in I_{\nu}} \int_{\sigma} f(t)\,dt.$$

Combining this inequality with 4.3.6, and letting $\delta \to 0$,

$$m(E_{\epsilon}^{+}) \leq \frac{16}{\lambda} \int_{-\infty}^{+\infty} f(t)\,dt.$$

By an analogous argument, we get

$$m(E_{\epsilon}^{-}) \leq \frac{16}{\lambda} \int_{-\infty}^{+\infty} f(t)\,dt.$$

Finally letting $\epsilon \to 0$, these two inequalities yield

$$m\left\{x : \sup_{\epsilon} |H_{\epsilon}(x, f)| > \frac{\lambda}{\pi}\right\} \leq \frac{32}{\lambda} \int_{-\infty}^{+\infty} f(t)\,dt.$$

We can thus obtain 4.3.4 with $c = 64/\pi$.

It should be clear by now how we can proceed to establish that the limit

4.3.9 $$H(x, f) = \lim_{\epsilon \to 0} H_\epsilon(x, f)$$

exists almost everywhere. Indeed, by writing

$$H_\epsilon(x, f) = \int_\epsilon^\infty \frac{f(x - t) - f(x + t)}{t}\, dt$$

we see that when $f(x)$ is a continuously differentiable function of compact support, 4.3.9 will actually exist for all x.

We then set

$$\Omega(x, f) = \limsup_{\epsilon_1, \epsilon_2 \to 0} |H_{\epsilon_1}(x, f) - H_{\epsilon_2}(x, f)|,$$

and obtain from 4.3.4,

4.3.10 $$m\{x : \Omega(x, f) > \epsilon\} \leq \frac{4c}{\epsilon} \int_{-\infty}^{+\infty} |f|\, dx.$$

Since, again $\Omega(x, f)$ is not affected if we subtract from f an arbitrary continuously differentiable function of compact support, we conclude from 4.3.10 that

$$m\{x : \Omega(x, f) > \epsilon\} = 0 \qquad \forall \quad \epsilon > 0.$$

Thus the family of functions $H_\epsilon(x, f)$ is a.e. "Cauchy" as $\epsilon \to 0$. We define $H(x, f)$ then by 4.3.9 when the limit exists and set it equal to zero, say, for all other x.

By 4.2.1 we have as well for almost all x,

4.3.11 $$H(x, f) = \lim_{y \to 0} Q_y(x, f) = \lim_{y \to 0} \frac{1}{\pi} \int_{-\infty}^{+\infty} f(t) \frac{x - t}{(x - t)^2 + y^2}\, dt.$$

At this point it is important to note that when f is square integrable in $(-\infty, +\infty)$, then $H(x, f)$ is also the limit of $H_y(x, f)$ as well as $Q_y(x, f)$ in the L_2 sense. To show this, we need the identity

4.3.12 $$\frac{1}{\pi} \int_{-\infty}^{+\infty} \frac{t_1 - x}{(t_1 - x)^2 + y_1^2} \frac{x - t_2}{(x - t_2)^2 + y_2^2}\, dx = -\frac{y_1 + y_2}{(t_1 - t_2)^2 + (y_1 + y_2)^2},$$

which is easily established by use of elementary methods.

This given, using the abbreviations $H_y(f)$, $Q_y(f)$, etc., for $H_y(x, f)$, $Q_y(x, f)$, etc., we can write

4.3.13
$$\int_{-\infty}^{+\infty} [Q_{y+y_1}(f) - Q_{y_1}(f)]^2\, dx$$
$$= \int_{-\infty}^{+\infty} f[P_{2y+2y_1}(f) - 2P_{y+2y_1}(f) + P_{2y_1}(f)]\, dx.$$

The interchange of order of integration needed to establish this relation is easily justified when f is of compact support. In Remark 4.2.3 we have observed that

4.3.14
$$\lim_{y\to 0} \int_{-\infty}^{+\infty} |P_y(f) - f|^2\, dx = 0.$$

Thus, letting $y_1 \to 0$ in 4.3.13, by 4.3.11 and Fatou's lemma we obtain

$$\int_{-\infty}^{+\infty} [Q_y(f) - H(f)]^2\, dx \le \int_{-\infty}^{+\infty} |f||P_{2y}(f) - 2P_y(f) + f|dx.$$

So, finally, 4.3.14 gives

4.3.15
$$\lim_{y\to 0} \int_{-\infty}^{+\infty} |Q_y(f) - H(f)|^2\, dx = 0.$$

To establish

$$\lim_{y\to 0} \int_{-\infty}^{+\infty} |H_y(f) - H(f)|^2\, dx = 0,$$

we need only observe that 4.2.3, by an easy argument, implies that when f is square integrable,

$$\lim_{y\to 0} \int_{-\infty}^{+\infty} |H_y(f) - Q_y(f)|^2\, dx = 0.$$

Important corollaries of the result in 4.3.15 are the two following theorems.

THEOREM 4.3.2. *If $f(x)$ is square integrable, then $H(f)$ is also square integrable and indeed*

4.3.16
$$\int_{-\infty}^{+\infty} [H(f)]^2\, dx = \int_{-\infty}^{+\infty} |f|^2\, dx;$$

furthermore, we have for all such f,

4.3.17 $$H(H(f)) = -f.$$

PROOF. To establish 4.3.16, we simply note that the identity in 4.3.12 implies that

4.3.18 $$\int_{-\infty}^{+\infty} [Q_y(f)]^2\,dx = \int_{-\infty}^{+\infty} fP_{2y}(f)\,dx.$$

Thus, from 4.3.14, we get

$$\lim_{y\to 0} \int_{-\infty}^{+\infty} [Q_y(f)]^2\,dx = \int_{-\infty}^{+\infty} f^2\,dx.$$

Combining this result with 4.3.15, 4.3.16 immediately follows.

To get 4.3.17, we start with the inequality

4.3.19 $$\|H(H(f)) + f\|_2 \le \|H(H(f)) - Q_y(H(f))\|_2 + \|Q_y(H(f)) - Q_y(Q_y(f))\|_2 + \|Q_y(Q_y(f)) + f\|_2.$$

Then note that 4.3.12 gives

$$Q_y(Q_y(f)) = -P_{2y}(f),$$

and 4.3.18 implies

$$\int_{-\infty}^{+\infty} [Q_y(f)]^2\,dx \le \int_{-\infty}^{+\infty} f^2\,dx$$

for all square-integrable f. Going back to 4.3.19, we obtain then

$$\|H(H(f)) + f\|_2 \le \|H(H(f)) - Q_y(H(f))\|_2 + \|H(f) - Q_y(f)\|_2 + \|P_{2y}(f) - f\|_2.$$

Thus 4.3.17 follows by letting $y \to 0$ in this relation, using 4.3.14 for f and 4.3.15 for both f and Hf.

THEOREM 4.3.3. *If f and g are square integrable, then*

4.3.20 $$\int_{-\infty}^{+\infty} f(x)H(x, g)\,dx = -\int_{-\infty}^{+\infty} g(x)H(x, f)\,dx.$$

PROOF. A change of order of integration in the expression

$$\int_{-\infty}^{+\infty} f(x)Q_y(x, g)\,dx = \frac{1}{\pi}\int_{-\infty}^{+\infty} f(x)\int_{-\infty}^{+\infty} \frac{x-t}{(x-t)^2 + y^2} g(t)\,dt\,dx,$$

which is easily justified when f and g are both of compact support, yields the identity

4.3.21 $$\int_{-\infty}^{+\infty} f(x)Q_y(x, g)\, dx = -\int_{-\infty}^{+\infty} g(x)Q_y(x, f)\, dx.$$

This given, 4.3.20 immediately follows from 4.3.15 upon letting $y \to 0$ in 4.3.21.

4.4 THE EXPONENTIAL ESTIMATE FOR THE MAXIMAL HILBERT TRANSFORM

A good portion of our effort in the previous sections has been directed toward laying the foundations necessary to establish the following theorem, which plays an essential role in Carleson's work.

THEOREM 4.4.1. *There is a positive constant c such that, if $f(x)$ is any essentially bounded function whose support is contained in an interval of length A, then*

4.4.1 $$m\{x : H^*(x, f) \geq c\lambda \|f\|_\infty\} \leq \frac{A}{\lambda} e^{-\lambda}.$$

PROOF. Note first that for any fixed $\lambda_0 > 0$, 4.3.4 yields

$$m\{x : H^*(x, f) > ce^{\lambda_0}\|f\|_\infty \lambda\} \leq \frac{A}{\lambda} e^{-\lambda_0} \leq \frac{A}{\lambda} e^{-\lambda}$$

for all $\lambda \leq \lambda_0$. Thus we need only establish 4.4.1 for all sufficiently large λ.

Trivially, we may restrict ourselves to the case $\|f\|_\infty \leq 1$. This given, we shall establish first the inequality

4.4.2 $$m\{x : |H(x, f)| > \lambda\} \leq \frac{c_1 A e^{-\lambda/c_2}}{\lambda},$$

for some constants $c_1, c_2 > 0$, for $\|f\|_\infty \leq 1$ and λ sufficiently large.

We will then show that 4.4.2 implies a similar inequality for $H^*(x, f)$. Thereafter 4.4.1 can be obtained by a suitable change of scale in λ.

To derive 4.4.2 we set

$$E_\lambda^+ = \{x : H(x, f) \geq \lambda\}, \qquad E_\lambda^- = \{x : H(x, f) \leq -\lambda\},$$

then proceed to estimate the measures of these two sets separately. We shall carry this out only for E_λ^+, since the arguments concerning E_λ^- are analogous.

We start with the standard estimate

$$\lambda m(E_\lambda^+) \leq \int_{E_\lambda^+} H(x, f)\, dx = \int_{-\infty}^{+\infty} \chi_{E_\lambda^+}(x) H(x, f)\, dx.$$

Since both $\chi_{E_\lambda^+}$ and $H(x, f)$ are square integrable, from Theorem 4.3.3 we get

$$\lambda m(E_\lambda^+) \leq -\int_{-\infty}^{+\infty} f(x) H(x, \chi_{E_\lambda^+})\, dx.$$

At this point it is tempting to try and separate f from $H(x, \chi_{E_\lambda^+})$ in this integral by a use of Hölder's inequality. If we do that, we obtain, for $(1/p) + (1/q) = 1$,

4.4.3 $$\lambda m(E_\lambda^+) \leq A^{1/q}\left[\int_{-\infty}^{+\infty} |H(x, \chi_{E_\lambda^+})|^p\, dx\right]^{1/p}.$$

At this moment, however, it is not even clear that $H(x, \chi_{E_\lambda^+})$ should be in L_p. To establish this fact, we write

4.4.4 $$\frac{1}{p}\int_{-\infty}^{+\infty} |H(x, \chi_{E_\lambda^+})|^p\, dx = \int_0^\infty m\{x : |H(x, \chi_{E_\lambda^+})| > \mu\}\mu^{p-1}\, d\mu.$$

For convenience, let us just write E for E_λ^+. Note then that Theorem 4.3.1 gives

$$m\{x : |H(x, \chi_E)| > \mu\} \leq \frac{c}{\mu} m(E),$$

while from Theorem 4.3.2 we easily deduce

$$m\{x : |H(x, \chi_E)| > \mu\} \leq \frac{1}{\mu^2} m(E).$$

Using the first of these relations for $\mu < 1$ in 4.4.4 and the second for $\mu > 1$, we obtain

4.4.5 $$\int_{-\infty}^{+\infty} |H(x, \chi_E)|^p \leq \left(\frac{cp}{p-1} + \frac{p}{2-p}\right) m(E) \leq 2cq\, m(E),$$

provided

4.4.6 $$q = \frac{p}{p-1} \geq 2 + \frac{1}{c}.$$

Substituting 4.4.5 in 4.4.3 and canceling the factor $[m(E_\lambda^+)^{1/p}$, we get

$$\lambda[m(E_\lambda^+)]^{1/q} \leq A^{1/q}[2cq]^{1/p},$$

or better yet, since $q/p = q - 1$,

$$m(E_\lambda^+) \leq \frac{A}{2cq}\left(\frac{2cq}{\lambda}\right)^q.$$

Upon setting $q = \lambda/2ce$, which in view of 4.4.6 is permissible as long as

4.4.7 $$\lambda \geq 2ce\left[2 + \frac{1}{c}\right],$$

we finally obtain

$$m(E_\lambda^+) \leq \frac{eA}{\lambda} e^{-\lambda/2ce}$$

Precisely the same inequality can be obtained for E_λ^-, upon changing f into $-f$ in our arguments. Thus we can conclude that, when 4.4.7 holds,

$$m\{x : |H(x, f)| > \lambda\} \leq \frac{2eA}{\lambda} e^{-\lambda/2ce}.$$

And this is of the form 4.4.2, as was to be shown.

We are thus only left to show that a similar result holds for $H^*(x, f)$ as well.

The argument here follows very much the lines used in the proof of Theorem 4.3.1. Again, by means of the decomposition $f = f^+ - f^-$, we can reduce ourselves to having to consider only the case $f \geq 0$. This given, for a fixed λ, we set

$$E_\epsilon^+ = \{x : \sup_{\eta \geq \epsilon} H_\eta(x, f) \geq \lambda\}, \qquad E_\epsilon^- = \{x : \sup_{\eta \geq \epsilon} -H_\eta(x, f) \geq \lambda\},$$

and proceed to estimate the measure of these sets.

Let us work on E_ϵ^+. We note again that E_ϵ^+ can be covered by the intervals I for which

$$\frac{1}{\pi}\int_{^cI}\frac{f(t)\,dt}{c(I)-t}\geq\lambda.$$

Since E_ϵ^+ is compact, a finite number of these intervals cover it. By the interval selection lemma, we can thus find disjoint intervals $I_1, I_2,\ldots, I_n$ such that

4.4.8 (a) $$\frac{1}{\pi}\int_{^cI_v}\frac{f(t)\,dt}{c(I_v)-t}\,dt\geq\lambda \qquad \text{for } v=1,2,\ldots,n;$$

(b) $$m(E_\epsilon^+)\leq 2\sum_{v=1}^{n} m(I_v).$$

Set

$$f_v(x)=\begin{cases} f(x) & \text{for } x\in I_v,\\ 0 & \text{for } x\notin I_v.\end{cases}$$

Since f is nonnegative, the function

$$g_v(x)=H(x,f)-H(x,f_v)=\frac{1}{\pi}\int_{^cI_v}\frac{f(t)\,dt}{x-t}$$

is nonincreasing in I_v. By 4.4.8(a), this function is greater than or equal to λ at the center of I_v, then it will stay that way throughout the left half of I_v. We can therefore conclude that

$$\tfrac{1}{2}\sum_{v=1}^{n} m(I_v)\leq m\left\{x : H(x,f)>\frac{\lambda}{2}\right\}+\sum_{v=1}^{n} m\left\{x : H(x,f_v)<\frac{-\lambda}{2}\right\}.$$

From 4.4.2, we obtain then

$$\sum_{v=1}^{n} m(I_v)\leq\frac{4c_1A}{\lambda}e^{-\lambda/c_2}+\sum_{v=1}^{n} m(I_v)\frac{4c_1}{\lambda}e^{-\lambda/c_2}$$
$$\leq\frac{4c_1A}{\lambda}e^{-\lambda/c_2}+\tfrac{1}{2}\sum_{v=1}^{n} m(I_v),$$

provided λ is sufficiently large. This gives

$$\sum_{v=1}^{n} m(I_v)\leq\frac{8c_1A}{\lambda}e^{-\lambda/c_2},$$

which, combined with 4.4.8(b), yields

$$m(E_\epsilon^+) \le \frac{16c_1}{\lambda} A e^{-\lambda/c_2}.$$

Precisely the same inequality can be obtained for E_ϵ^-. We then deduce

$$m\{x : \sup_{\eta \ge \epsilon} |H_\eta(x, f)| \ge \lambda\} \le \frac{32c_1 A}{\lambda} e^{-\lambda/c_2},$$

and the desired estimate is finally obtained by letting $\epsilon \to 0$.

Thus the proof of the theorem is complete.

REMARK 4.4.1. It is perhaps worthwhile to point out another path by which the inequality

4.4.9 $$m\{x : H^*(x, f) > c\lambda\} \le \frac{A}{\lambda} e^{-\lambda}$$

can be obtained from the analogous inequality involving $H(x, f)$.

The idea is to start from the formula

4.4.10 $$Q_{y_1+y_2}(x, f) = P_{y_1}(x, Q_{y_2}(f)) = \frac{1}{\pi}\int_{-\infty}^{+\infty} \frac{y_1}{(x-t)^2 + y_1^2} Q_{y_2}(t, f)\, dt,$$

which is valid for all y_1, $y_2 > 0$ and follows immediately from the elementary identity

$$\frac{x-t}{(x-t)^2 + (y_1+y_2)^2} = \frac{1}{\pi}\int_{-\infty}^{+\infty} \frac{y_1}{(x-\sigma)^2 + y_1^2} \frac{\sigma - t}{(\sigma - t)^2 + y_2^2}\, d\sigma.$$

When f is square integrable, upon passing to the limit in 4.4.10 as $y_2 \to 0$, 4.3.15 gives

4.4.11 $$Q_y(x, f) = P_y(x, H(f)).$$

This given, the inequality

$$|H_y(x, f)| \le |H_y(x, f) - Q_y(x, f)| + |Q_y(x, f)|,$$

combined with 4.2.2 and 4.4.11 yields

$$|H_y(x, f)| \le P_y(x, |f|) + P_y(x, |H(f)|).$$

So that Theorem 4.2.1 then gives the remarkable inequality

4.4.12 $$H^*(x, f) \le \theta(x, f) + \theta(x, H(f)).$$

The estimate in 4.4.9 is then obtained by establishing an analogous estimate for both $\theta(x, f)$ and $\theta(x, H(f))$.

REMARK 4.4.2. Although they will not be needed in our later considerations, we might as well deduce also the following very important classical results.

THEOREM 4.4.2. *For every $p > 1$, there is a constant $c_p > 0$ such that*

$$4.4.13 \qquad \int_{-\infty}^{+\infty} [H^*(x, f)]^p \, dx \leq c_p \int_{-\infty}^{+\infty} |f|^p \, dx.$$

In view of 4.4.12 and 4.2.14, this inequality is an immediate consequence of the following famous result of M. Riesz [34].

THEOREM 4.4.3. *For every $p > 1$, we have a constant $c_p > 0$ such that*

$$4.4.14 \qquad \int_{-\infty}^{+\infty} [H(x, f)]^p \, dx \leq c_p \int_{-\infty}^{+\infty} |f|^p \, dx.$$

Perhaps the most interesting path to 4.4.14, in view of the material we have thus far accumulated, is one which is due to Marcinkiewicz [43]. The idea here is to deduce the L_p estimate in 4.4.14 from the two estimates

$$4.4.15 \quad \text{(a)} \quad m\{x : |H(x, f)| > \lambda\} \leq \frac{c}{\lambda} \int_{-\infty}^{+\infty} |f| \, dx,$$

$$\text{(b)} \quad \int_{-\infty}^{+\infty} [H(x, f)]^2 \, dx \leq \int_{-\infty}^{+\infty} |f|^2 \, dx,$$

via an "interpolation" result.

We shall state the basic result of Marcinkiewicz in the special cases needed here, for too general a setting would carry us too far out of the present context.

THEOREM 4.4.4. *Suppose for two exponents $1 \leq p_1 < p_2$ we have shown that, for all bounded f, say,*

$$4.4.16 \qquad m\{x : |H(x, f)| > \lambda\} \leq \frac{c_1}{\lambda^{p_1}} \int_{-\infty}^{+\infty} |f|^{p_1} \, dx,$$

$$4.4.17 \qquad m\{x : |H(x, f)| > \lambda\} \leq \frac{c_2}{\lambda^{p_2}} \int_{-\infty}^{+\infty} |f|^{p_2} \, dx,$$

then we must also have for all $p_1 < p < p_2$,

4.4.18 $$\int_{-\infty}^{+\infty} |H(x, f)|^p \, dx \leq 2^p \left(\frac{c_1 p}{p - p_1} + \frac{c_2 p}{p_2 - p} \right) \int_{-\infty}^{+\infty} |f|^p \, dx.$$

PROOF. Breaking up f in the form

$$f = f^\lambda + f_\lambda$$

with

$$f^\lambda = \begin{cases} f & \text{if } |f| \leq \lambda, \\ 0 & \text{if } |f| > \lambda, \end{cases} \qquad f_\lambda = \begin{cases} f & \text{if } |f| > \lambda, \\ 0 & \text{if } |f| \leq \lambda, \end{cases}$$

and using 4.4.16 on f_λ and 4.4.17 on f^λ, we get

$$m\{x : |H(x, f)| > 2\lambda\} \leq \frac{c_1}{\lambda^{p_1}} \int_{-\infty}^{+\infty} |f_\lambda|^{p_1} \, dx + \frac{c_2}{\lambda^{p_2}} \int_{-\infty}^{+\infty} |f^\lambda|^{p_2} \, dx.$$

Multiplying this inequality by λ^{p-1} and integrating with respect to λ from 0 to ∞, upon using Fubini's theorem, we get

$$\int_{-\infty}^{+\infty} \left(\int_0^{|H(x,f)|/2} \lambda^{p-1} \, d\lambda \right) dx \leq c_1 \int_{-\infty}^{+\infty} |f|^{p_1} \left(\int_0^{|f|} \lambda^{p-p_1-1} \, d\lambda \right) dx$$
$$+ c_2 \int_{-\infty}^{+\infty} |f|^{p_2} \left(\int_{|f|}^{\infty} \frac{d\lambda}{\lambda^{p_2-p+1}} \right) dx,$$

from which 4.4.18 immediately follows.

Let us go back now to the proof of Theorem 4.4.3. The inequalities 4.4.15 yield 4.4.16 and 4.4.17 for $p_1 = 1$ and $p_2 = 2$; thus from Theorem 4.4.4 we get

4.4.19 $$\int_{-\infty}^{+\infty} |H(x, f)|^p \, dx \leq c2^p \left[\frac{p}{p-1} + \frac{p}{2-p} \right] \int_{-\infty}^{+\infty} |f|^p \, dx,$$

for all $1 < p < 2$.

To obtain 4.4.14 for all other values of p, we make use of a "duality" argument. This goes as follows. We start with the identity (Theorem 4.3.3)

4.4.20 $$\int_{-\infty}^{+\infty} f(x) H(x, g) \, dx = - \int_{-\infty}^{+\infty} g(x) H(x, f) \, dx,$$

which we have shown to be valid for all square-integrable functions f and g. Then, by Hölder's inequality, 4.4.20 and 4.4.19 give

4.4.21 $$\left|\int_{-\infty}^{+\infty} f(x)H(x, g)\,dx\right| \leq \|g\|_q \left[2^p c\left(\frac{p}{p-1} + \frac{p}{2-p}\right)\int_{-\infty}^{+\infty} |f|^p\,dx\right]^{1/p},$$

where

$$q = \frac{p}{p-1}.$$

Since 4.4.21, fixed g, must hold for arbitrary f, we deduce

4.4.22 $$\int_{-\infty}^{+\infty} [H(x, g)]^q\,dx \leq 2^q c^{q/p}\left(\frac{p}{p-1} + \frac{p}{2-p}\right)^{q/p} \int_{-\infty}^{+\infty} |g|^q\,dx,$$

for all $q > 2$.

We have thus obtained 4.4.14 for all values of $p > 1$. However, the constants involved still leave something to be desired. Indeed, in both 4.4.19 and 4.4.22, the constants go to ∞ as the exponent approaches 2. This should not be the case for the best possible constants since *we do have* 4.4.15(b). This unpleasant feature, however, can be removed by a further use of Theorem 4.4.4, upon interpolating between $p_1 = \frac{3}{2}$ and $p_2 = 3$, say.

Finally, it is worthwhile to note that for $q \geq 3$ the inequality in 4.4.22 can be written in the form

4.4.23 $$\int_{-\infty}^{+\infty} |H(x, g)|^q\,dx \leq (cq)^q \int_{-\infty}^{+\infty} |g|^q\,dx.$$

REMARK 4.4.3. An operator T defined on the simple functions of a measure space $(\Omega, \mathscr{F}, \mu)$, satisfying an inequality such as

4.4.24 $$\mu\{x : |Tf| > \lambda\} \leq \frac{c}{\lambda^p}\int_\Omega |f|^p\,d\mu,$$

is said to be of "weak type (p, p)."

If T satisfies

4.4.25 $$\int_\Omega |Tf|^p\,d\mu \leq c\int_\Omega |f|^p\,d\mu,$$

then T is said to be of "strong type (p, p)." The inequality 4.4.25 is in general more demanding than 4.4.24. Indeed, when T is the Hilbert transform operator, we do have 4.4.24 for $p = 1$, but it can be shown that 4.4.25 is false for $p = 1$.

The Marcinkiewicz theorem allows us to conclude, under a rather general setup, that an operator which is simultaneously of weak types (p_1, p_1) and (p_2, p_2) for some $1 \leq p_1 < p_2 < \infty$ must necessarily be of strong type (p, p) for every $p_1 < p < p_2$.

Since the inequality in 4.4.23 does, in fact, imply the exponential estimate in 4.4.2 it would be interesting to know if, in reverse, 4.4.23 itself can be derived from the two inequalities

4.4.26 (a) $$m\{x : |H(x, f)| > \lambda\} \leq \frac{c}{\lambda} \int_{-\infty}^{+\infty} |f|\, dx,$$

(b) $$m\{x : |H(x, f)| > c\|f\|_\infty \lambda\} \leq \frac{A}{\lambda} e^{-\lambda},$$

by methods similar to those used in the proof of Theorem 4.4.4. This would amount to an "interpolation" between weak type (1, 1) and a sort of "weak type (∞, ∞)."

It turns out that the inequalities in 4.4.26 are *by themselves* not sufficient to imply the estimates

4.4.27 $$\int_{-\infty}^{+\infty} |H(x, f)|^p\, dx \leq c_p \int_{-\infty}^{+\infty} |f|^p\, dx.\dagger$$

However, if we use the additional fact that $H(x, f)$ is *invariant under translation*, then a proof of 4.4.27 can be obtained in this fashion.

In short, the following "interpolation" theorem can be established.

THEOREM 4.4.5. *Let T be a sublinear operator defined on the simple functions of a finite measure space $(\Omega, \mathscr{F}, \mu)$ and let T commute with a family Σ of invertible measure preserving transformations which "mixes" Ω (in the sense of Section 1.2). Suppose that T satisfies*

4.4.28 (a) $$\mu\{x : |Tf| > \lambda\} \leq \frac{c}{\lambda} \int_\Omega |f|\, d\mu,$$

(b) $$\mu\{x : |Tf| > \lambda\|f\|_\infty\} \leq ce^{-\lambda}.$$

† An example in point was produced by C. Preston.

Then for every $1 < p < \infty$ *there is a constant* c_p *such that*

$$\int_{\Omega} |Tf|^p \, d\mu \leq c_p \int_{\Omega} |f|^p \, d\mu.$$

To be sure, this result does not directly apply to our Hilbert transform $H(x, f)$, but it does apply to the Hilbert transform operator relative to the circle group. In this form, Theorem 4.4.5 can be derived from Stein's continuity principle.†

We shall leave this derivation to the reader. Before closing this section, we would like to point out that implicit in the work of Stein and Weiss [40] is a sort of "weak type (∞, ∞)" inequality which can be used for interpolation purposes without further hypotheses. This is an inequality of the type

$$\frac{\mu\{x : |Tf| > \lambda \| f \|_{\infty}\}}{\mu\{\text{support of } f\}} \leq h(\lambda),$$

where $h(\lambda)$ is only restricted to satisfy the condition

$$\int_0^{\infty} \lambda^p h(\lambda) \, d\lambda < \infty, \qquad \forall \quad p > 1.$$

Stein and Weiss have also shown, by methods similar to those used in the proof of Loomis' lemma, that indeed the Hilbert transform satisfies the exponential estimate 4.4.26(b) with

$$A = \text{meas support of } f.$$

Thus their work contains still a further proof of the L_p estimates for the Hilbert transform.

Finally, we would like to add that the reader with a good background in the classical theory of functions can find a very lucid exposition of most of the results concerning the Hilbert transform we have presented here in a recent book by Katznelson [23].

Complex variable methods lead to these results in what is perhaps the shortest and most elegant fashion.

We have adopted the real variable approach here, however, because these methods are more susceptible of generalizations to higher dimensions than complex variable methods are and also to keep in line with the strictly real variable content of the rest of these lecture notes.

† We owe this observation to G. Weiss.

4.5 TWO LEMMAS OF CARLESON

There are two lemmas which play a crucial role in Carleson's work. Since these lemmas and especially some of the estimates which follow from them are of independent interest, it is worthwhile to set them apart from the rest of our treatment.

We shall start with the more elementary of these results.

LEMMA 4.5.1. *Let $\varphi(t)$ be a function that is twice continuously differentiable in an interval ω and suppose that for some constant A we have*

4.5.1 $$|\varphi(t)| \le A, \qquad |\varphi''(t)| \le \frac{A}{|\omega|^2} \qquad \forall \quad t \in \omega.\dagger$$

Then, for any function $f(t)$ that is integrable in ω, we have

4.5.2 $$\left|\frac{1}{|\omega|}\int_\omega \varphi(t)e^{+2\pi i n t/|\omega|} f(t)\,dt\right| \le cA \sum_{\mu=-\infty}^{+\infty} \frac{1}{1+\mu^2}\left|\frac{1}{|\omega|}\int_\omega \exp\left[\frac{2\pi i}{|\omega|}\left(n-\frac{\mu}{2}\right)t\right] f(t)\,dt\right|,$$

where c is a universal constant.

PROOF. We shall carry out our arguments under the assumption that

$$\omega = [-\tfrac{1}{2}, \tfrac{1}{2}],$$

for the general case can be reduced to this case by a suitable change of variables.

This given, the estimate in 4.5.2 will immediately follow if we establish that we can write $\varphi(t)$, for all $t \in [-\frac{1}{2}, \frac{1}{2}]$, in the form

4.5.3 $$\varphi(t) = \sum_{\mu=-\infty}^{+\infty} \gamma_\mu e^{-\pi i \mu t},$$

with

4.5.4 $$|\gamma_\mu| \le c\frac{A}{1+\mu^2}.$$

To this end, note that if in $[-\frac{1}{2}, \frac{1}{2}]$

$$|\varphi(t)| \le A \qquad \text{and} \qquad |\varphi''(t)| \le A,$$

† If ω is an interval, we denote its length by $|\omega|$.

then we must also have there

$$|\varphi'(t)| \leq 3A.$$

Let us extend the definition of $\varphi(t)$ for all $|t| \geq \frac{1}{2}$ by setting

$$\varphi(t) = \varphi(\tfrac{1}{2}) + (t - \tfrac{1}{2})\varphi'(\tfrac{1}{2}) + \frac{(t - \frac{1}{2})^2}{2}\varphi''(\tfrac{1}{2})$$

when $t \geq \frac{1}{2}$, and

$$\varphi(t) = \varphi(-\tfrac{1}{2}) + (t + \tfrac{1}{2})\varphi'(-\tfrac{1}{2}) + \frac{(t + \frac{1}{2})^2}{2}\varphi''(-\tfrac{1}{2})$$

when $t \leq -\frac{1}{2}$. The resulting extended function will then satisfy for all $|t| \leq 1$.

4.5.5
$$|\varphi(t)| \leq 3A,\qquad |\varphi'(t)| \leq 3A,\qquad |\varphi''(t)| \leq A.$$

We now pick once and for all a function $\Delta(t)$ which is twice continuously differentiable in $[-1, 1]$ and satisfies

4.5.6 (a) $\Delta(t) \equiv 1$ for $|t| \leq \frac{1}{2}$,

(b) $\Delta(t) \equiv 0$ for $|t| \geq \frac{3}{4}$,

and set

$$\psi(t) = \Delta(t)\varphi(t).$$

From the estimates in 4.5.5, we deduce that

$$|\psi(t)| \leq cA,\qquad |\psi'(t)| \leq cA,\qquad |\psi''(t)| \leq cA,$$

where c is a constant depending only on the choice of $\Delta(t)$.

Because of 4.5.6(b) the function $\psi(t)$ in $[-1, 1]$ can be thought as the restriction of a twice continuously differentiable function, that in periodic of period 2. We thus have

$$\psi(t) = \sum_{\mu=-\infty}^{+\infty} e^{-\pi i\mu t/2} \int_{-1}^{1} e^{\pi i\mu\sigma}\psi(\sigma)\, d\sigma;$$

two integrations by parts then give

$$\left| \tfrac{1}{2} \int_{-1}^{1} e^{\pi i \mu \sigma} \psi(\sigma)\, d\sigma \right| \leq \frac{cA}{1 + \mu^2}.$$

Since for $|t| \leq \frac{1}{2}$, by 4.5.6(a),

$$\psi(t) \equiv \varphi(t),$$

we get both 4.5.3 and 4.5.4.

The lemma is thus established.

We can now proceed to the next estimate.

LEMMA 4.5.2. *If Ω is any finite partition of an interval ω into intervals σ and we set*

$$g_\Omega(x) = \sum_{\sigma \in \Omega} \int_\sigma \frac{|\sigma|\, dt}{|\sigma|^2 + (x - t)^2},$$

then for any $\lambda > 0$, we have

4.5.7 $$m\{x \in \omega : g_\Omega(x) \geq \lambda\} \leq \frac{6|\omega|}{\lambda} e^{-\lambda/6}.$$

PROOF. Let $\alpha(x)$ be a nonnegative function whose support is in ω and such that $\alpha(x) \log^+ \alpha(x)$ is integrable. From the definition of $g_\Omega(x)$ we get

$$\int_\omega \alpha(x) g_\Omega(x)\, dx = \sum_{\sigma \in \Omega} \int_\sigma \int_\omega \frac{|\sigma| \alpha(x)}{|\sigma|^2 + (x - t)^2}\, dx\, dt$$
$$= \sum_{\sigma \in \Omega} \int_\sigma P_{|\sigma|}(t, \alpha)\, dt,$$

and Theorem 4.2.1 yields

$$\int_\omega \alpha(x) g_\Omega(x)\, dx \leq \sum_{\sigma \in \Omega} \int_\sigma \theta(x, \alpha)\, dx = \int_\omega \theta(x, \alpha)\, dx.$$

Applying the inequality in 4.2.15 with $f = \alpha$, we obtain

4.5.8 $$\int_\omega \alpha(x) g_\Omega(x)\, dx \leq 2|\omega| + 4 \int_\omega \alpha(x) \log^+ \alpha(x)\, dx.$$

Let $E = \{x \in \omega : g_\Omega(x) > \lambda\}$ and set for some constant $\alpha \geq 1$,

$$\alpha(x) = \alpha \chi_E(x).$$

The inequality 4.5.8 then gives

$$\alpha\lambda m(E) \leq 2|\omega| + 4\alpha \log \alpha\, m(E).$$

We thus see that to obtain 4.5.7, we need only set $\alpha = e^{\lambda/6}$.

To write our estimates in the precise form they will be used in the arguments which follow, we need one additional rather elementary result.

LEMMA 4.5.3. *Let $\delta(x)$ be a nonnegative measurable function defined in an interval ω and such that*

4.5.9
$$m\{x \in \omega : \delta(x) > c\lambda\} \leq |\omega| \frac{1}{\lambda} e^{-\lambda};$$

then $e^{\delta(x)/2c}$ is integrable and

4.5.10
$$\frac{1}{|\omega|} \int_\omega e^{\delta(x)/2c}\, dx \leq 1 + e.$$

PROOF. We start with the inequality

4.5.11
$$e^{\delta/2c} \leq e + \int_1^\infty \chi\left(\frac{\delta}{2c}, \lambda\right) e^\lambda\, d\lambda,$$

where, as usual, we have set

$$\chi(u, v) = \begin{cases} 1 & \text{if } u \geq v, \\ 0 & \text{if } u < v. \end{cases}$$

Note then that by our hypothesis 4.5.9,

$$\frac{1}{|\omega|} \int_1^\infty m\left\{x \in \omega : \frac{\delta(x)}{2c} > \lambda\right\} e^\lambda\, d\lambda \leq \int_1^\infty \frac{1}{2\lambda} e^{-\lambda}\, d\lambda < 1.$$

Thus, by Fubini's theorem, we get

$$\frac{1}{|\omega|} \int_\omega \int_1^\infty \chi\left(\frac{\delta(x)}{2c}, \lambda\right) e^\lambda\, d\lambda\, dx = \frac{1}{|\omega|} \int_1^\infty \int_\omega \chi\left(\frac{\delta(x)}{2c}, \lambda\right) dx\, e^\lambda\, d\lambda < 1.$$

In view of 4.5.11, this shows that $e^{\delta(x)/2c}$ is integrable and that indeed 4.5.10 holds as well.

For both the maximal Hilbert transform (Theorem 4.4.1) and for the function $g_\Omega(x)$ (Lemma 4.5.2) we have precisely an estimate of the type 4.5.9; therefore we immediately obtain the following two corollaries.

THEOREM 4.5.1. *There is a universal constant $c > 0$ such that if $f(x)$ is any bounded measurable function whose support is contained in an interval ω, then*

4.5.12
$$\frac{1}{|\omega|}\int_{\omega} e^{H^*(x,f)/c\|f\|_\infty}\,dx \leq c.$$

THEOREM 4.5.2. *There is a universal constant $c > 0$† such that if Ω is any partition of an interval ω into intervals σ and*

$$g_\Omega(x) = \sum_{\sigma\in\Omega}\int_{\sigma}\frac{|\sigma|\,dt}{|\sigma|^2 + (x-t)^2},$$

then

$$\frac{1}{|\omega|}\int_{\omega} e^{g_\Omega(x)/c}\,dx \leq c.$$

4.6 CARLESON'S FUNDAMENTAL STEP

In this section we shall prove a theorem which provides the fundamental step in Carleson's proof. However, before we can do this we need to introduce some notation.

We recall that if σ is an interval, we denote its center and its length by $c(\sigma)$ and $|\sigma|$, respectively. This given, the interval

$$\left[c(\sigma) - \frac{|\sigma|}{4},\, c(\sigma) + \frac{|\sigma|}{4}\right]$$

will be called the "mid-half" of σ.

Starting from a given interval ω, which here and after will be kept fixed, we introduce classes Σ_ν of dyadic intervals associated with ω by the following procedure.

We subdivide ω into two equal intervals and denote by

$$\sigma_0^{(1)},\ \sigma_0^{(2)}$$

its two halves labeled as they are encountered from left to right.

Similarly, we subdivide each of these into equal parts, obtaining intervals

$$\sigma_1^{(1)},\ \sigma_1^{(2)},\ \sigma_1^{(3)},\ \sigma_1^{(4)}.$$

† We can actually take $c = 12$.

Proceeding inductively, having partitioned ω, for $v \geq 1$, into subintervals

$$\sigma_v^{(1)}, \sigma_v^{(2)}, \ldots, \sigma_v^{(2^{v+1})},$$

we subdivide, in turn, each of these into two equal intervals and denote, for each $1 \leq i \leq 2^{v+1}$, by

$$\sigma_{v+1}^{(2i-1)}, \sigma_{v+1}^{(2i)}$$

the two halves of $\sigma_v^{(i)}$, again labeled as they are encountered from left to right.

We let Σ_v, for each $v \geq 0$, denote the collection of intervals

$$\sigma_{v+1}^{(i)} \cup \sigma_{v+1}^{(i+1)} \qquad \text{for } 1 \leq i < 2^{v+2}.$$

For any interval σ contained in ω, it will be convenient to denote by $\mathring{\sigma}$ the mid-half of σ minus the end points of the intervals $\sigma_v^{(i)}$.

This given, when $x \in \mathring{\omega}$, we can be sure that *for each* $v \geq 0$ there is a unique i such that

$$x \in \sigma_{v+2}^{(2i)} \cup \sigma_{v+2}^{(2i+1)}.$$

We define for such a v

$$\omega_v(x) = \sigma_{v+1}^{(i)} \cup \sigma_{v+1}^{(i+1)}.$$

In other words, $\omega_v(x)$ *is the unique interval of the class* Σ_v *which contains* x *in its mid-half.*

Our program is to show that given any square-integrable function $f(x)$ of compact support, we have

4.6.1 $$\sup_{n \geq 2} \frac{1}{\log \log n} \left| \int_\omega e^{2\pi i n t/|\omega|} \frac{f(t)\, dt}{x - t} \right| < \infty \quad \text{a.e. in } \mathring{\omega}.$$

As we have indicated in our preliminaries, this is all that is needed to obtain Carleson's "$\log \log n$" result.

Carleson actually shows that 4.6.1 holds when $f(x)$ p-integrable and $p > 1$. In these notes we shall then start with a function $f(x)$ which, at first, is assumed to be only integrable, then add further hypotheses as we need them.

The function $f(x)$ being fixed, we introduce two interval functions $C_n(\sigma)$ and $D_n(\sigma)$ by setting

$$C_n(\sigma) = \sum_{\mu=-\infty}^{+\infty} \frac{1}{1+\mu^2} \frac{1}{|\sigma|} \left| \int_\sigma \exp\left[\frac{\pi i}{2|\sigma|}\left(\frac{\mu}{2} - n\right)\right] f(t)\, dt \right|$$

and

$$D_n(\sigma) = C_n(\sigma^{(1)}) + C_n(\sigma^{(2)}) + C_n(\sigma^{(3)}) + C_n(\sigma^{(4)}),$$

where $\sigma^{(1)}, \sigma^{(2)}, \sigma^{(3)}, \sigma^{(4)}$ give the decomposition of σ into four equal intervals.

We are finally in a position to state and prove Carleson's fundamental theorem.

THEOREM 4.6.1. *Let $f(x)$ be an integrable function and ω_1 be one of the intervals $\sigma_{\nu_1}^{(i)} \cup \sigma_{\nu_1}^{(i+1)}$. For each $n \geq 1$, when x varies in $\mathring{\omega}_1$ it is possible to define an integer-valued function $\nu(x)$ with the following properties:*

(a) $\nu_1 + 1 \leq \nu(x) \leq \nu_1 + k_0$, *where*

$$\frac{\log n}{\log 2} < k_0 \leq \frac{\log n}{\log 2} + 1.$$

(b) *If we set $\omega'(x) = \omega_{\nu(x)}(x)$, the function*

$$R_n(x, \omega_1) = \int_{\omega_1 - \omega'(x)} e^{-2\pi int/|\omega_1|} \frac{f(t)\,dt}{x - t}$$

satisfies the inequality

4.6.2
$$\frac{1}{|\omega_1|} \int_{\mathring{\omega}_1} e^{|R_n(x,\omega_1)|/cD_n(\omega_1)}\,dx \leq c,$$

where c is a universal constant.

(c) *If we set* $n(x) = \left[n \dfrac{|\omega'(x)|}{|\omega_1|}\right]$,†

we have, whenever $n(x) \geq 1$,

4.6.3
$$D_{n(x)}(\omega(x)) \geq 2D_n(\omega_1).$$

Note. At first reading, it might be worthwhile at this point to skip over the proof of this theorem and appreciate its significance by seeing first how it is used to derive the "log log n" estimate.

PROOF. We shall begin by constructing a partition Ω of the given interval $\omega_1 = \sigma_{\nu_1}^{(i_1)} \cup \sigma_{\nu_1}^{(i_1+1)}$ by intervals $\sigma_\nu^{(i)}$ with $\nu \geq \nu_1 + 1$ according to the following procedure.

† $[\alpha]$ is to indicate the integral part of α.

We let the first "waiting class" P_1 consist of the four equal intervals

$$\sigma_{\nu_1+1}^{(2i_1-1)},\ \sigma_{\nu_1+1}^{(2i_1)},\ \sigma_{\nu_1+1}^{(2i_1+1)},\ \sigma_{\nu_1+1}^{(2i_1+2)}.$$

Each interval σ in P_1 is then subdivided into its two equal subintervals σ' and σ''. If we have

$$C_{[n/2]}(\sigma') \geq 2D_n(\omega_1) \qquad \text{or} \qquad C_{[n/2]}(\sigma'') \geq 2D_n(\omega_1),$$

we put σ in Ω. If not, we put both σ' and σ'' into the second waiting class P_2.

We do this for each $\sigma \in P_1$.

Note that all the intervals of P_2 will be of size

$$\frac{1}{2^{1+2}}|\omega_1| = \frac{1}{2^{\nu_1+3}}|\omega|.$$

We then proceed by induction. Having defined the kth waiting class P_k containing intervals σ of size

$$\frac{1}{2^{1+k}}|\omega_1|$$

such that

4.6.4 $$C_{[n/2^{k-1}]}(\sigma) = C_{[4|\sigma|n/|\omega_1|]}(\sigma) < 2D_n(\omega_1),$$

to construct the $(k+1)$st waiting class P_{k+1}, we split each $\sigma \in P_k$ into its two equal subintervals σ' and σ'' and put $\sigma \in \Omega$ if one of the two inequalities

$$C_{[n/2^k]}(\sigma') \geq 2D_n(\omega_1) \qquad \text{or} \qquad C_{[n/2^k]}(\sigma'') \geq 2D_n(\omega_1)$$

holds. Otherwise we put both σ' and σ'' in P_{k+1}.

We stop this procedure when we run out of intervals (i.e., P_k is empty) or when $2^k > n$, whichever comes first. In the latter case we dump all the intervals of P_k into Ω.

We see then that the size of the last intervals put with Ω is at least

$$|\omega|\frac{1}{2^{\nu_1+k_0+1}},$$

where

$$\frac{\log n}{\log 2} < k_0 \leq \frac{\log n}{\log 2} + 1.$$

It is clear that Ω gives a partition of ω_1.

We are now in a position to define the function $\nu(x)$ whose existence is asserted by the theorem.

If x is in $\mathring{\omega}_1$† we simply let $\nu(x)$ be the *smallest* ν such that $\omega_\nu(x)$ has one of its halves in Ω.

We shall check first that condition 4.6.3 is satisfied. This is immediately verified: Since one of the halves of $\omega_{\nu(x)}(x)$ is in Ω, one of its quarters σ satisfies the inequality

$$C_{[n(4|\sigma|/|\omega_1|)]}(\sigma) \geq 2D_n(\omega_1).$$

This implies 4.6.3.

Before proceeding to obtain the estimate in 4.6.2 we observe that the function $\nu(x)$ has the following two basic properties:

(1) *For x in $\mathring{\omega}_1$, $\omega_{\nu(x)}(x)$ is a union of intervals of Ω.*

In particular, we deduce that also $\omega_1 - \omega_{\nu(x)}(x)$ is such a union. For convenience we let $\Omega(x)$ denote the intervals of Ω that are in $\omega_1 - \omega_{\nu(x)}(x)$. This given we further have

(2) *Each interval $\sigma \in \Omega(x)$ has a distance from x that is at least $\frac{1}{2}|\sigma|$.*

Both these properties follow immediately from the definition of $\nu(x)$.

For instance, if for some $\sigma \in \Omega(x)$, (2) were not true, then such interval would be of greater length than one half of $\omega_{\nu(x)}(x)$, but that would be in conflict with the minimality of $\nu(x)$.

To establish the estimate in 4.6.2. we write first

$$\begin{aligned} R_n(x, \omega_1) &= \sum_{\sigma \in \Omega(x)} \int_\sigma e^{-2\pi i n t/|\omega_1|} \frac{f(t)\, dt}{x - t} \\ &= \sum_{\sigma \in \Omega(x)} \int_\sigma \frac{E_n(\sigma)\, dt}{x - t} \\ &\quad + \sum_{\sigma \in \Omega(x)} \int_\sigma (e^{-2\pi i n t/|\omega_1|} f(t) - E_n(\sigma)) \frac{dt}{x - t}, \end{aligned}$$

with

$$E_n(\sigma) = \frac{1}{|\sigma|} \int_\sigma e^{-2\pi i n t/|\omega_1|} f(t)\, dt.$$

† That is if x is in the mid-half of ω_1 but is not one of the end points of the intervals $\sigma_\nu^{(i)}$.

Since the functions

$$e^{-2\pi int/|\omega_1|}f(t),\ E_n(\sigma)$$

have equal integrals over σ, we can further write $R_n(x, \omega_1)$ in the form

$$R_n(x, \omega_1) = R_n^{(1)}(x, \omega_1) + R_n^{(2)}(x, \omega_1) + R_n^{(3)}(x, \omega_1),$$

where we have set

$$R_n^{(1)}(x, \omega_1) = \sum_{\sigma \in \Omega(x)} \int_\sigma \frac{E_n(\sigma)\,dt}{x - t},$$

$$R_n^{(2)}(x, \omega_1) = \sum_{\sigma \in \Omega(x)} \int_\sigma e^{-2\pi int/|\omega_1|}f(t)\left(\frac{1}{x - t} - \frac{1}{x - c(\sigma)}\right) dt,$$

$$R_n^{(3)}(x, \omega_1) = \sum_{\sigma \in \Omega(x)} \int_\sigma E_n(\sigma)\left(\frac{1}{x - c(\sigma)} - \frac{1}{x - t}\right) dt.\dagger$$

We shall then proceed to obtain an estimate of type 4.6.2 for each of these functions separately.

(a) *The estimate for* $R_n^{(1)}(x, \omega_1)$. Introducing the function $E_n(t)$ by setting

$$E_n(t) = \begin{cases} E_n(\sigma) & \text{when } t \in \sigma \text{ and } \sigma \in \Omega, \\ 0 & \text{otherwise,} \end{cases}$$

we see that, for some universal constant c, we have

$$|R_n^{(1)}(x, \omega_1)| = \left| \int_{\omega_1 - \omega'(x)} \frac{E_n(t)\,dt}{x - t} \right| \leq H^*(x, E_n) + c\|E_n\|_\infty,$$

where the last term comes from the fact that x is not precisely the center of $\omega_{v(x)}(x)$.

From Theorem 4.5.1 we deduce that there is a universal constant c such that

4.6.5
$$\frac{1}{|\omega_1|} \int_{|\mathring{\omega}_1|} e^{|R_n^{(1)}(x,\omega_1)|/c\|E_n\|_\infty}\,dt \leq c.$$

We thus need to estimate $\|E_n\|_\infty$. To this end we write

$$E_n(\sigma) = \frac{1}{|\sigma|} \int_\sigma e^{-2\pi imt/|\sigma|} e^{-2\pi i\lambda t/|\sigma|} f(t)\,dt,$$

† Recall that $c(\sigma)$ denotes the center of σ.

with

$$m = \tfrac{1}{4}\left[\frac{4|\sigma|n}{|\omega_1|}\right] \qquad \text{and} \qquad \lambda = \frac{n|\sigma|}{|\omega_1|} - m.$$

Note then that since $\lambda \leq \tfrac{1}{4}$, from Lemma 4.5.1 with $\varphi(t) = e^{-2\pi i\lambda t/|\sigma|}$, $A = \pi^2/4$, $\omega = \sigma$, and $n = m$, we get

$$|E_n(\sigma)| \leq \frac{c}{|\sigma|}\sum_{\mu}\frac{1}{1+\mu^2}\left|\int_\sigma \exp\left[\frac{2\pi i}{|\sigma|}\left(m - \frac{\mu}{2}\right)t\right]f(t)\,dt\right|,$$

from which we easily derive

$$|E_n(\sigma)| \leq \frac{16c}{|\sigma|}\sum_{\mu}\frac{1}{1+\mu^2}\left|\int_\sigma \exp\left[\frac{\pi i}{2|\sigma|}\left(4m - \frac{\mu}{2}\right)t\right]f(t)\,dt\right|.$$

In other words,

$$|E_n(\sigma)| \leq cC_{[(4|\sigma|/|\omega_1|)n]}(\sigma).$$

The inequality 4.6.4, which is valid for all $\sigma \in \Omega$, then implies that

4.6.6 $$\|E_n\|_\infty \leq cD_n(\omega_1).$$

Substituting this estimate in 4.6.5 we see that the function $R_n^{(1)}(x, \omega_1)$ does indeed satisfy an inequality of type 4.6.2.

(b) *Estimates for* $R_n^{(2)}(x, \omega_1)$ *and* $R_n^{(3)}(x, \omega_1)$. We start with $R_n^{(3)}(x, \omega_1)$. From 4.6.6 we get

$$|R_n^{(3)}(x, \omega_1)| \leq cD_n(\omega_1)\sum_{\sigma\in\Omega(x)}\int_\sigma \frac{\tfrac{1}{2}|\sigma|\,dt}{|x-t||x-c(\sigma)|}.$$

However, a simple geometric argument based upon property (2) of the partition Ω yields for all $\sigma \in \Omega(x)$,

$$\frac{1}{|x-c(\sigma)||x-t|} \leq \frac{4}{|\sigma|^2 + (x-t)^2} \qquad \forall \quad t \in \sigma.$$

Thus

$$|R_n^{(3)}(x, \omega_1)| \leq 2cD_n(\omega_1)\sum_{\sigma\in\Omega}\int_\sigma \frac{|\sigma|\,dt}{|\sigma|^2 + (x-t)^2},$$

and Theorem 4.5.2 then shows that the function $R_n^{(3)}(x, \omega_1)$ must also satisfy an inequality of type 4.6.2.

The function $R_n^{(2)}(x, \omega_1)$ can be estimated in a similar way if we can show that for all $\sigma \in \Omega(x)$ we have as well

4.6.7
$$\left| \int_\sigma e^{-2\pi i n t/|\omega_1|} f(t) \left(\frac{1}{x - t} - \frac{1}{x - c(\sigma)} \right) dt \right|$$
$$\leq c D_n(\omega_1) \int_\sigma \frac{|\sigma|\, dt}{|\sigma|^2 + (x - t)^2}.$$

Remarkably enough this inequality can be obtained by another application of Lemma 4.5.1. To see this we write the first integral in 4.6.7 again in the form

4.6.8
$$\int_\sigma e^{-2\pi i m t/|\sigma|} f(t) \varphi(t)\, dt,$$

where now

$$\varphi(t) = e^{-2\pi i \lambda t/|\sigma|} \left(\frac{1}{x - t} - \frac{1}{x - c(\sigma)} \right),$$

with

$$\lambda = \frac{|\sigma| n}{|\omega_1|} - m \qquad \text{and} \qquad m = \tfrac{1}{4} \left[\frac{4|\sigma| n}{|\omega_1|} \right],$$

as before.

Property (2) of the partition Ω then yields, for fixed x,

$$|\varphi(t)| \leq c \frac{|\sigma|}{(x - c(\sigma))^2},$$

$$|\varphi''(t)| \leq \frac{c}{|\sigma|} \frac{1}{(x - c(\sigma))^2}.$$

It is also easily seen that we have

$$\frac{|\sigma|}{(x - c(\sigma))^2} \leq 4 \int_\sigma \frac{dt}{|\sigma|^2 + (x - t)^2}.$$

A use of Lemma 4.5.1 then yields

$$\frac{1}{|\sigma|}\left|\int_\sigma e^{-2\pi int/|\omega_1|}f(t)\left(\frac{1}{x-t}-\frac{1}{x-c(\sigma)}\right)dt\right|$$

$$\leq c\int_\sigma \frac{dt}{|\sigma|^2+(x-t)^2}\sum_\mu \frac{1}{1+\mu^2}$$

$$\times\ \frac{1}{|\sigma|}\left|\int_\sigma \exp\left[\frac{2\pi i}{|\sigma|}\left(m-\frac{\mu}{2}\right)t\right]f(t)\,dt\right|.$$

This given, 4.6.7. can be obtained by steps similar to those used in deriving the inequality 4.6.6.

In conclusion, we have shown that each of the functions $R_n^{(i)}(x, \omega_1)$ $(i = 1, 2, 3)$ satisfies an inequality of type 4.6.2. By Hölder's inequality, the same must hold true for their sum.

Theorem 4.6.1. is thus established.

4.7 THE "log log n" ESTIMATE

We are finally in a position to prove Carleson's "log log n" result. For a fixed interval ω, and a large integer N, we shall set

$$Q_N(x, f) = \sup_{n \leq 2^N}\left|\int_\omega e^{-2\pi int/|\omega|}\frac{f(t)\,dt}{x-t}\right|.$$

In this section we shall show that for some universal constant c we have

4.7.1 $$\lim_{N\to\infty}\left(\frac{Q_N(x, f)}{\theta(x, f)} - c\log N\right) = -\infty \quad \text{a.e.}$$

for all square-integrable f. We shall also indicate how the same result can be obtained for all f in L_p for every $p > 1$.

The key inequality we are all set up to prove can be expressed by the following theorem.

THEOREM 4.7.1. *For any f in L_p $(p > 1)$ we have*

4.7.2 $$Q_N(x, f) \leq c\theta(x, f) + cH^*(x, f) + K_N(x, f),$$

where, as before, $\theta(x, f)$ and $H^*(x, f)$ denote, respectively, the Hardy–Littlewood function and the maximal Hilbert transform of f and

$K_N(x, f)$ is a function satisfying the inequality

4.7.3 $$\int_{\mathring{\omega}} \theta^p e^{K_N/c_p\theta}\, dx \le c_p N \int_\omega |f|^p\, dx.$$

Here c is a universal constant and c_p is a constant depending only on p.

The result in 4.7.1 can be easily derived from 4.7.2 and 4.7.3 upon dividing 4.7.3 by N^3 and summing with respect to N.†

In proving Theorem 4.7.1 we shall keep f, ω and N fixed, while n will denote throughout the rest of this section an integer satisfying

$$0 \le n \le 2^N.$$

Theorem 4.7.1 will be obtained by repeated applications of Theorem 4.6.1. We shall establish the inequality in 4.7.3 in full for $p = 2$, and shall later indicate what modifications are necessary to obtain the general result.

We start by applying Theorem 4.6.1 and obtain accordingly the integer-valued function $\nu_1(x)$. We then write, for x in the mid-half of ω:

$$\int_\omega e^{-2\pi int/|\omega|} \frac{f(t)\, dt}{x - t} = \int_{\omega'(x)} e^{-2\pi int/|\omega|} \frac{f(t)\, dt}{x - t} + R_n(x, \omega).$$

The idea is to apply once more Theorem 4.6.1 to the expression

$$\int_{\omega'} e^{-2\pi int/|\omega|} \frac{f(t)\, dt}{x - t},$$

where for a moment ω' is considered fixed. Again x is in the mid-half of ω', however to be exactly in the same situation as before we need to replace the exponential

$$e^{-2\pi int/|\omega|}$$

by one of the form

$$e^{-2\pi in't/|\omega'|}.$$

It is again Lemma 4.5.1 which enables us to carry out such a step. We set

4.7.4 $$n' = \left[\frac{n}{|\omega|}|\omega'|\right],$$

† There is no loss in assuming $\theta(x, f) > 0$ in ω, since by trivial manipulations we can always reduce ourselves to such a case.

and note that the difference

$$\Delta = \int_{\omega'} e^{2\pi i n(x-t)/|\omega|} \frac{f(t)\,dt}{x-t} - \int_{\omega'} e^{2\pi i n'(x-t)/|\omega'|} \frac{f(t)\,dt}{x-t},$$

can be written in the form

$$\Delta = e^{2\pi i n' x/|\omega'|} \int_{\omega'} \frac{e^{2\pi i (n/|\omega| - n'/|\omega'|)(x-t)} - 1}{x-t} e^{-2\pi i n' t/\omega'} f(t)\,dt.$$

This given, an application of Lemma 4.5.1, with

$$\varphi(t) = \frac{e^{2\pi i (n/|\omega| - n'/|\omega'|)(x-t)} - 1}{x-t}$$

and

$$A = 2\pi \left| \frac{n}{|\omega|} - \frac{n'}{|\omega'|} \right| \leq \frac{2\pi}{|\omega'|},$$

gives

$$|\Delta| \leq c \sum_{\mu} \frac{1}{1+\mu^2} \frac{1}{|\omega'|} \left| \int_{\omega'} \exp\left[\frac{2\pi i}{|\omega'|} \left(n' - \frac{\mu}{2} \right) t \right] f(t)\,dt \right|.$$

Since we have

$$\int_{\omega'} e^{-2\pi i n t/|\omega|} \frac{f(t)\,dt}{x-t} = e^{-2\pi i n x/|\omega|} \Delta$$

$$+ \exp\left[2\pi i \left(\frac{n'}{|\omega'|} - \frac{n}{|\omega|} \right) x \right] \int_{\omega'} e^{-2\pi i n' t/|\omega'|} \frac{f(t)\,dt}{x-t},$$

we therefore obtain

$$\left| \int_{\omega} e^{-2\pi i n t/|\omega|} \frac{f(t)\,dt}{x-t} \right| \leq \left| \int_{\omega'} e^{-2\pi i n' t/|\omega'|} \frac{f(t)\,dt}{x-t} \right| + cD_{n'}(\omega')$$

$$+ |R_n(x, \omega)|.$$

Now, there are two possibilities. Either $n' = 0$, in which case we stop our procedure. Or $n' \geq 1$, in which case we apply again Theorem 4.6.1 to the term

$$\int_{\omega'} e^{-2\pi i n' t/|\omega'|} \frac{f(t)\,dt}{x-t}.$$

We will thus be able to produce another integer-valued function $\nu_2(x)$, a subinterval $\omega''(x)$ of $\omega'(x)$, and an integer n'' such that

$$\left|\int_{\omega} e^{-2\pi i n t/|\omega|} \frac{f(t)\,dt}{x-t}\right| \leq \left|\int_{\omega''} e^{-2\pi i n'' t/|\omega''|} \frac{f(t)\,dt}{x-t}\right| + cD_{n''}(\omega'') + cD_{n'}(\omega') + |R_n(x,\omega)| + |R_{n'}(x,\omega')|.$$

If $n'' \neq 0$, we can carry out this step once more and obtain an estimate of the form

$$\left|\int_{\omega} e^{-2\pi i n t/|\omega|} \frac{f(t)\,dt}{x-t}\right| \leq \left|\int_{\omega''} e^{-2\pi i n'' t/|\omega''|} \frac{f(t)}{x-t}\right| + |R_n(x,\omega)| + |R_{n'}(x,\omega')| + |R_{n''}(x,\omega'')| + cD_{n'}(\omega'(x)) + cD_{n''}(\omega''(x)) + cD_{n'''}(\omega'''(x)).$$

To write the final estimate in a convenient form we need to introduce some auxiliary notation.

Set for each $-1 \leq \nu < N$

$$n_\nu = \left[\frac{n}{2^{\nu+1}}\right].$$

In other words, if

$$n = \epsilon_0 + \epsilon_1 2 + \cdots + \epsilon_{N-1} 2^{N-1}$$

is the binary expansion of n,

$$n_\nu = \epsilon_{\nu+1} + \cdots + \epsilon_{N-1} 2^{N-\nu-2}.$$

We then see that

$$n'(x) = \left[n \frac{|\omega'(x)|}{|\omega|}\right] = n_{\nu_1(x)}.$$

Moreover,

$$n''(x) = \left[n_{\nu_1(x)} \frac{|\omega''(x)|}{|\omega'(x)|}\right] = \left[\frac{\epsilon_{\nu_1(x)+1} 2^{\nu_1(x)+1} + \cdots + \epsilon_{N-1} 2^{N-1}}{2^{\nu_2(x)+1}}\right] = n_{\nu_2(x)}.$$

Similarly,

$$n'''(x) = n_{\nu_3(x)}.$$

Let us set also, for each $-1 \le \nu < N$,

$$e_n^{(\nu)}(x) = |R_n(x, \omega_\nu(x))| + cD_n(\omega_\nu(x)),$$

$$\gamma_n^{(\nu)}(x) = D_n(\omega_\nu(x)),$$

and

$$\chi_n^{(\nu)}(x) = \begin{cases} 1 & \text{if } \nu = -1 \text{ or } \nu = \nu_i(x) \text{ for some } i, \\ 0 & \text{otherwise.} \end{cases}$$

This given, it is easy to see that the procedure we have indicated eventually leads to the inequality

4.7.5

$$\left| \int_\omega e^{-2\pi i n t/|\omega|} \frac{f(t)\,dt}{x - t} \right| \le \left| \int_{\omega_N(x)} \frac{f(t)\,dt}{x - t} \right| + \sum_{\nu=-1}^{N-1} \chi_n^{(\nu)}(x) e_{n_\nu}^{(\nu)}(x).$$

We are now in a position to prove Theorem 4.7.1. Note first that, for any N,

$$\left| \int_{\omega_N(x)} \frac{f(t)\,dt}{x - t} \right| \le cH^*(x, f) + c\theta(x, f).†$$

To prove Theorem 4.7.1 we then need only show that the function

$$K_N(x, f) = \sup_{n \le 2^N} \sum_{\nu=-1}^{N-1} \chi_n^{(\nu)}(x) e_{n_\nu}^{(\nu)}(x)$$

satisfies the inequality in 4.7.3.

Let us assume first that $p = 2$. In this case our functions, $e_n^{(\nu)}$, $\gamma_n^{(\nu)}$, and $\chi_n^{(\nu)}$, satisfy the following inequalities:

4.7.6 (a) $$\int_\sigma \exp[e_n^{(\nu)}(t)/c\gamma_n^{(\nu)}(t)]\,dt \le c|\sigma| \qquad \forall \quad \sigma \in \Sigma_{\nu+1},$$

(b) $$\sum_n [\gamma_n^{(\nu)}(x)]^2 \le c\frac{1}{|\omega_\nu(x)|} \int_{\omega_\nu(x)} |f(t)|^2\,dt,$$

(c) $$\sum_{\nu=-1}^{N-1} \chi_n^{(\nu)}(x) \sqrt{\gamma_{n_\nu}^{(\nu)}(x)} \le c\sqrt{\theta(x, f)},$$

(d) $$\gamma_n^{(\nu)}(x) \le c\theta(x, f).$$

† The term in $\theta(x, f)$ comes in because x may not be precisely the mid-point of $\omega_N(x)$.

The first of these inequalities is an immediate consequence of the inequality in 4.6.2.

Going back to the definition of $C_n(\sigma)$, from Bessel's inequality we easily obtain

4.7.7 $$\sum_n [C_n(\sigma)]^2 \leq c \int_\sigma f^2(t)\,dt.$$

Thus a similar inequality holds for $D_n(\sigma)$ as well and 4.7.6(b) must necessarily follow.

Similarly 4.7.6(d) is a consequence of the trivial inequality

$$C_n(\sigma) \leq \left(\sum_\mu \frac{1}{1+\mu^2}\right)\frac{1}{|\sigma|}\int_\sigma |f(t)|\,dt.$$

Finally, we observe that the inequality 4.6.3, which was assured in Theorem 4.6.1, implies that each time $\chi_n^{(v)}(x) \neq 0$ the quantity $\gamma_{n_v}^{(v)}(x)$ is guaranteed to double in size. It therefore follows that the sum in 4.7.6(c) is no larger than a fixed constant times its largest term. However, by 4.7.6(d), such a term is no larger than a constant multiple of $\sqrt{\theta(x, f)}$.† This proves 4.7.6(c).

Before getting on with our proof of Theorem 4.7.1 it is worthwhile to have an idea of the role that each of these inequalities is going to play.

We are to estimate

$$K_N(x, f) = \sup_{n \leq 2^N} \sum_{v=-1}^{N-1} \chi_n^{(v)}(x) e_{n_v(x)}^{(v)}.$$

Clearly, in 4.7.6(c) we have a similar sum and the estimate there is very nice indeed. Essentially, 4.7.6(a) says that $\gamma_n^{(v)}$ and $e_n^{(v)}$ are comparable in a sense, so roughly speaking 4.7.6(c) can be used to estimate $K_N(x, f)$. The trouble with this heuristic argument is that $e_n^{(v)}$ may still be considerably larger than $\gamma_{n_v}^{(v)}$ in a set which could vary quite wildly with n. The inequality in 4.7.6(b) keeps this variability under control and enables us to achieve the crucial goal, i.e., to make the final estimate *independent of n*.

† Of course in the preceding argument the square root could be replaced with any power $0 < \alpha < 1$. But then $c = c_\alpha$. In the arguments which follow it is immaterial what power is chosen here.

It may be said that this is the difficulty which has frustrated all previous attempts at the convergence result and which has been admirably overcome by Carleson.

Let us get on now with the actual estimates.

We start by setting

$$M_N^{(\nu)}(x) = \max_{n \le 2^N} \frac{e_n^{(\nu)}(x)}{\sqrt{\gamma_n^{(\nu)}(x)}},$$

$$M_N(x) = \max_{-1 \le \nu < N} \left\{ \max_{n \le 2^N} \frac{e_n^{(\nu)}(x)}{\sqrt{\gamma_n^{(\nu)}(x)}} \right\} = \max_{-1 \le \nu < N} M_N^{(\nu)}(x).$$

Then, by 4.7.6(c), we trivially get

$$\sum_{\nu=-1}^{N-1} \chi_n^{(\nu)}(x) e_{n_\nu}^{(\nu)}(x) \le M_N(x) \sum_{\nu=-1}^{N-1} \chi_n^{(\nu)}(x) \sqrt{\gamma_{n_\nu}^{(\nu)}(x)} \le c M_N(x) \sqrt{\theta(x, f)}.$$

We thus have

$$\int_{\bar\omega} \theta^2 e^{K_N/\lambda c \theta}\, dt \le \int_{\bar\omega} \theta^2 \exp\left(\frac{M_N}{\lambda\sqrt{\theta}}\right) dt.$$

Here λ is a fixed constant whose size will soon be determined.

Using the function

$$\psi(u) = \begin{cases} 0 & \text{for } u \le 1, \\ 1 & \text{for } u > 1, \end{cases}$$

we write further

$$\int_{\bar\omega} \theta^2 e^{K_N/\lambda c \theta}\, dt \le \int_{\bar\omega} \theta^2 e^4\, dt + \int_{\bar\omega} \theta^2 \psi\left(\frac{M_N}{4\lambda\sqrt{\theta}}\right) \exp\left(\frac{M_N}{\lambda\sqrt{\theta}}\right) dt.$$

From Theorem 4.2.3 we obtain

$$\int_{\omega} \theta^2(x, f)\, dx \le c \int_{\omega} |f|^2\, dx.$$

So we are left with having to estimate the integral

$$I = \int_{\bar\omega} \theta^2 \psi\left(\frac{M_N}{4\lambda\sqrt{\theta}}\right) \exp\left(\frac{M_N}{\lambda\sqrt{\theta}}\right) dt.$$

Now, trivially,

$$I \leq \sum_{\nu=-1}^{N-1} \int_{\mathring{\omega}} \theta^2 \psi\left(\frac{M_N^{(\nu)}}{4\lambda\sqrt{\theta}}\right) \exp\left[\frac{M_N^{(\nu)}}{\lambda\sqrt{\theta}}\right] dt$$

$$= \sum_{\nu=-1}^{N-1} \sum_{\sigma}^{(\nu)} \int_{\sigma} \theta^2 \psi\left(\frac{M_N^{(\nu)}}{4\lambda\sqrt{\theta}}\right) \exp\left[\frac{M_N^{(\nu)}}{\lambda\sqrt{\theta}}\right] dt,$$

where $\sum_{\sigma}^{(\nu)}$ indicates a sum carried over those intervals σ of the type $\sigma_{\nu+2}^{(i)}$ which are in $\mathring{\omega}$. Very crudely, we get

4.7.8 $$I \leq \sum_{\nu=-1}^{N-1} \sum_{\sigma}^{(\nu)} \sum_{n} \int_{\sigma} \theta^2 \psi\left(\frac{e_n^{(\nu)}}{4\lambda\sqrt{\gamma_n^{(\nu)}}\sqrt{\theta}}\right) \exp\left[\frac{e_n^{(\nu)}}{\lambda\sqrt{\gamma_n^{(\nu)}}\sqrt{\theta}}\right] dt.$$

Now, note that the integrand is different from zero only when

$$\frac{e_n^{(\nu)}}{4\lambda\sqrt{\gamma_n^{(\nu)}}} \geq \sqrt{\theta},$$

and we also have [by 4.7.6(d)]

$$\gamma_n^{(\nu)} \leq c\theta.$$

Thus

$$\theta^2 \exp\left[\frac{e_n^{(\nu)}}{\lambda\sqrt{\gamma_n^{(\nu)}}\sqrt{\theta}}\right] \leq \frac{(\gamma_n^{(\nu)})^2}{c^2} \exp\left[\frac{\sqrt{c}\,e_n^{(\nu)}}{\lambda\gamma_n^{(\nu)}}\right].$$

This is because $x^4 e^{A/x} \leq y^4 e^{A/y}$ when $y \leq x \leq A/4$. Substituting in 4.7.8,

$$I \leq \sum_{\nu=-1}^{N-1} \sum_{\sigma}^{(\nu)} \sum_{n} \frac{1}{c^2} \int_{\sigma} (\gamma_n^{(\nu)})^2 \exp\left[\frac{\sqrt{c}\,e_n^{(\nu)}}{\lambda\gamma_n^{(\nu)}}\right] dt.$$

Now observe that, by its very definition $\gamma_n^{(\nu)}$ is constant in each interval of type $\sigma_{\nu+2}^{(i)}$. So, by 4.7.6(a) we get

$$\int_{\sigma} (\gamma_n^{(\nu)})^2 \exp\left[\frac{\sqrt{c}\,e_n^{(\nu)}}{\lambda\gamma_n^{(\nu)}}\right] dt \leq c|\sigma| \int_{\sigma} (\gamma_n^{(\nu)})^2\, dt,$$

provided

$$\frac{\lambda}{\sqrt{c}} \geq c.$$

Thus, using 4.7.6(b), we finally obtain

$$I \leq \frac{1}{c} \sum_{\nu=-1}^{N-1} \sum_{\sigma}^{(\nu)} \int_{\sigma} \frac{|\sigma|}{|\omega_\nu(x)|} \left(\int_{\omega_\nu(x)} f^2(t)\, dt \right) dx \leq cN \int_{\omega} f^2(t)\, dt.$$

This proves Theorem 4.7.1 for $p = 2$.

We shall indicate briefly how the same type of argument can be used to obtain the same result for $1 < p < 2$. For convenience let $q = p/(p-1)$.

The idea is to replace 4.7.6(b) by an inequality of the form

4.7.9 $$\sum_n [\gamma_n^{(\nu)}(x)]^q \leq c_p \left\{ \frac{1}{|\omega_\nu(x)|} \int_{\omega_\nu(x)} |f|^p\, dt \right\}^{q/p},$$

which is a consequence of the Hausdorff–Young theorem (see [43], theorem (2.3), p. 101).

We then start with the integral

$$\int_{\mathring{\omega}} \theta^p e^{(p/q)(K_N/\lambda c\theta)}\, dt,$$

but now, we use the cutoff function

$$\psi\left(\frac{M_N}{2q\lambda\sqrt{\theta}}\right).$$

This leads us to estimate the integral

$$I = \int_{\mathring{\omega}} \theta^p \psi\left(\frac{M_N}{2q\lambda\sqrt{\theta}}\right) \exp\left(\frac{pM_N}{q\lambda\sqrt{\theta}}\right) dt.$$

However, this time we are led to the inequality

$$I \leq \sum_{\nu=-1}^{N-1} \sum_{\sigma}^{(\nu)} \left\{ \sum_n \int_{\sigma} \theta^q \psi\left(\frac{e_n^{(\nu)}}{2q\lambda\sqrt{\gamma_n^{(\nu)}}\sqrt{\theta}}\right) \times \exp\left[\frac{q}{p} \frac{e_n^{(\nu)}}{\lambda\sqrt{\gamma_n^{(\nu)}}\sqrt{\theta}}\right] dt \right\}^{q/p} |\sigma|^{1-(p/q)}.$$

The proof from this point on proceeds as before except that now we use the inequality

$$x^{2q} e^{A/x} \leq y^{2q} e^{A/y},$$

which is valid when $0 < y \leq x \leq A/2q$.

Thus our arguments are complete.

Remarks. Since the work [8] of Carleson appeared, some additional results on the almost everywhere convergence of trigonometric and orthogonal series have been obtained. Notable are the works of R. Hunt and P. Billard.

Hunt [20] was able to extend Carleson's convergence result to all L_p's. Indeed, Hunt established the remarkable "strong" estimate

$$\int_{-\pi}^{\pi} [S^*(x, f)]^p \, dx \leq c_p \int_{-\pi}^{\pi} |f|^p \, dx$$

for all $p > 1$.

It thus appears that the operator

$$S^*(x, f) = \sup_n |S_n(x, f)|$$

is only slightly worse than the maximal Hilbert transform. It must be worse, since, in view of Kolmogorov's classical example (Zygmund [43], Vol. 1, Chap. III), there are f's in L_1 such that

$$S^*(x, f) = \infty$$

everywhere.

In this respect it is worth noting that Kahane and Katznelson ([22] and [24]) have shown that any set of measure zero can be the divergence set of the Fourier series of a continuous function. Thus, in a sense, Carleson's result is best possible.

We see already from the proof of the "$\log\log n$" result that Marcel Riesz's fundamental contributions to the theory of conjugate functions [34] play a crucial role in Carleson's work.

It is to be noted in this respect that Luzin, with remarkable premonition, apparently believed that a proof of the convergence result would depend on a study of the Hilbert transform integral.

Hunt's methods are essentially only a slight modification of Carleson's. The basic additional tool used by Hunt is an interpolation theorem of Stein and Weiss [40].

Billard [2] showed that it is possible to adapt Carleson's methods to prove the a.e. convergence result for Walsh series. The Walsh system is the natural completion of the Rademacher system.

In this setup Carleson's proof simplifies somewhat, but it is still far from being digestible. As matters stand now, these results can only be obtained via an arduous path, to say the least, and one would hope that in the nondistant future a simpler and more illuminating proof of Carleson's and Hunt's results will be found.

REFERENCES

[1] M. A. Akcoglu, "An ergodic lemma," *Proc. Am. Math. Soc.* **16**, 388–392 (1965).

[2] P. Billard, "Sur la convergence presque partout des séries de Fourier–Walsh des fonctions de l'espace $L^2(0, 1)$," *Studia Math.* **28**, 363–388 (1966–1967).

[3] E. Bishop, "A constructive ergodic theorem," *J. Math. Mech.* **17**(7), 631–640 (1968).

[4] E. Bishop, *Foundations of Constructive Analysis*, McGraw-Hill, New York, 1967.

[5] A. Brunel, "Sur une lemme ergodique voisin du lemme de E. Hopf, et sur une de ses applications," *Compt. Rend.* **256**, 5481–5484 (1963).

[6] D. L. Burkholder, "Maximal inequalities as necessary conditions for almost everywhere convergence," *Z. Wahrsch. Theorie* **3**, 75–88 (1964).

[7] D. L. Burkholder, "Successive conditional expectations of an integrable function," *Ann. Math. Statist.* **33**, 887–893 (1962).

[8] L. Carleson, "On convergence and growth of partial sums of Fourier series," *Acta Math.* (*Uppsala*) **116**(1–2), 135–157 (1966).

[9] R. V. Chacón, "The influence of the dissipative part of a general Markov process," *Proc. Am. Math. Soc.* **11**, 957–961 (1960).

[10] R. V. Chacón and D. Ornstein, "A general ergodic theorem," *Illinois J. Math.* **4**, 153–160 (1960).

[11] N. Dunford and J. Schwartz, *Linear Operators*, Vol. I, Wiley–Interscience, New York, 1958.

[12] A. Garsia, "Combinatorial inequalities and convergence of some orthonormal expansions," *Proceedings of the S.I.U. Conference on Orthogonal Expansions*, Southern Illinois Univ. Press, Carbondale, 1968, pp. 75–92.

[13] A. Garsia, "Existence of almost everywhere convergent rearrangements for Fourier series of L_2 functions," *Ann. Math.* **79**, 623–629 (1964).

[14] C. A. Greenhall, "L_q estimates for rearrangements of trigonometric series," *J. Math. Mech.* **16**, 311–319 (1966).

[15] R. Gundy, "Martingale theory and pointwise convergence of certain orthogonal series," *Trans. Am. Math. Soc.* **124**, 228–248 (1966).

[16] W. Hoeffding, "Probability inequalities for sums of bounded random variables," *J. Am. Math. Statist. Assoc.* **58**, 13–30 (1963).

[17] J. A. R. Holbrook, "The positive cone determined by a given subspace of functions," *Proceedings of the S.I.U. Conference on Orthogonal Expansions*, Southern Illinois Univ. Press, Carbondale, 1968, pp. 93–98.

[18] E. Hopf, "The general temporally discrete Markov process," *J. Rat. Mech. Anal.* **3**, 13–45 (1954).

[19] E. Hopf, "On the ergodic theorem for positive linear operators," *J. Math. Mech.* **205**, 101–106 (1961).

[20] R. A. Hunt, "On the convergence of Fourier series," *Proceedings of the S.I.U. Conference on Orthogonal Expansions*, Southern Illinois Univ. Press, Carbondale, 1968, pp. 235–255.

[21] R. Isaac, "A proof of the martingale convergence theorem," *Proc. Am. Math. Soc.* **16**, 842–844 (1965).

[22] J. P. Kahane and Y. Katznelson, "Sur les ensembles de divergence des séries trigonometriques," *Studia Math.* **26**, 305–306 (1966).

[23] Y. Katznelson, *An Introduction to Harmonic Analysis*, Wiley, New York, 1968.

[24] Y. Katznelson, "Sur les ensembles de divergence des séries trigonometriques," *Studia Math.* **26**, 301–304 (1966).

[25] A. Kolmogorov, "Sur les fonctions harmoniques conjugées et les séries de Fourier," *Fundamentals Math.* **7**, 23–28 (1925).

[26] A. Kolmogorov and G. S. Seliverstov, "Sur la convergence des séries de Fourier," *Compt. Rend.* **178**, 303–305 (1925).

[27] L. H. Loomis, "A note on the Hilbert transform," *Bull. Am. Math. Soc.* **52**, 1082–1086 (1946).

[28] N. N. Luzin, *Collected works*, Vol. I, or *Integral and Trigonometric Series*, M. L., Gostekhizdat, 1951.

[29] J. Marcinkiewicz, "Sur la convergence des séries orthogonales," *Studia Math.* **6**, 39–45 (1936).

[30] D. Menshov, "Sur les séries des fonctions orthogonales," *Fundamenta Math.* **4**, 82–105 (1923).

[31] D. Menshov, "Sur les séries des fonctions orthogonales," *Fundamenta Math.* **10**, 375–420 (1927).

[32] P. A. Meyer, "Théorie ergodique et potentiels," *Ann. Inst. Fourier* **15**, 89–96 (1965).

[33] P. A. Meyer, "Théorie ergodique et potentiels identification de la limite," *Ann. Inst. Fourier* **15**, 97–102 (1965).

[34] M. Riesz, "Sur les fonctions conjuguées," *Math. Z.* **27**(2), 218–244 (1927).

[35] B. Rosén, "Limit theorems for samplings from finite populations," *Arkiv Mat.* **5**, 383–424 (1965).

[36] B. Rosén, "On an inequality of Hoeffding," *Ann. Math. Statist.* **38** 382–392 (1967).

[37] S. Sawyer, "Maximal inequalities of weak type," *Ann. Math.* **84**(1), 157–173 (1966).

[38] F. Spitzer, "A combinatorial lemma and its application to probability theory," *Trans. Am. Math. Soc.* **82**, 323–339 (1956).

[39] E. M. Stein, "On limits of sequences of operators," *Ann. Math.* **74**, 140–170 (1961).

[40] E. M. Stein and G. Weiss, "An extension of a theorem of Marcinkiewicz and some of its applications," *J. Math. Mech.* **8**, 263–284 (1959).

[41] P. L. Uljanov, "Divergent Fourier series," *Russ. Math. Surv.* [*Trans. London Math. Soc.*, **16**, 1–75 (1961)].

[42] P. L. Uljanov, "Solved and unsolved problems in the theory of trigonometric and orthogonal series," *Russ. Math. Surv.* [*Trans. London Math. Soc.*, **19**, 1–62 (1964)].

[43] A. Zygmund, *Trigonometric Series*, Vols. I, II, Cambridge Univ. Press, New York, 2nd ed., 1959.